To all the brave souls who allow their pain to lead them to their purpose and their peace of mind.

Also, to leaders in their own right and the lives they inspire.

PRAISE FOR ALIGN YOUR BODY, ALIGN YOUR LIFE

A breath of fresh air. LisaBeth's story of healing and wellness is so needed. Eloquently written, with rigorous honesty and deep understanding. When so many paths to wellness involve avoidant spiritual bypass, LisaBeth has both feet on the ground, in beautiful reality. Infinite appreciation and gratitude.
—Lise Rondum

In the spirit of living a life well examined, LisaBeth forages unfettered and courageous, mining meaning from trauma, acknowledging excruciating trials on the pathway forward, and living in gratitude for what "is" each new day. With raw vulnerability, her sharing nourishes the reader with insightful hope into the personal possibilities we each surely possess.
—Mary Robin Jurkiewicz

A valuable book for all seeking healing, emPOWERment and striving to be better than they were yesterday! Your book provides me with a roadmap towards a thriving life of love, purpose and connectedness.
—Ham Brower, Founder of StandUpforHealth.org

LisaBeth has shared her journey that can inspire hope and offer courage to those daring and willing enough to chase recovery.
—Pastor Mark Farley, Founder of SCAA and Faith Through Works Fellowship

LisaBeth takes the reader with her on her journey—with all its ups and downs—to well-being. She not only talks the talk, but she walks the walk—and continues walking with the readers to encourage, guide, and support them on their own journeys as they use the self-paced exercises at the end of each chapter. LisaBeth is proof that with determination, tenacity, and hard work, seasoned with a sense of humor, everyone can create their own path of enlightenment, alignment, health, peace, and happiness. This practical and easy-to-use book belongs on everyone's bookshelf!
—Christel Autuori, MA, RYT, NBC-HWC, Institute for Holistic Health Studies Director, Western Connecticut State University

"Emotion was our first innate language," Bravo! LisaBeth has written a healing manifesto for all that is out of alignment in our lives!
—Jeanne Street God-based medium and author of Believe . . . Angels Don't Lie

There's so much about this book that justifies the read. Whether it's the gripping life anecdotes, the authentic exposure of the root causes of Lisabeth's own misalignment, or the useful strategies she shares at the end of each chapter, this book recounts the oh-so-relatable stories of how we spend the prime of our lives trying to free ourselves from decades of self-deprecation, self-inflicted pain and suffering and cauterized childhood trauma. At its core, this book is a wonderful tool for achieving balance and both inner and outer alignment through introspective auditing, exercising patience with the process of self-analysis, forgiveness, and active self-care, and coming out on the other side re-wired and wholly aligned with our true, authentic selves.
—Michele Thorne, author of Adding Raw Is Easy Recipe Book, and host of the FoodSlain podcast

Lisa hit the nail on the head! A good book to read if you're on a healing journey
—Cathy M.

Align Your Body Align Your Life is a truly honest depiction of the challenging yet beautiful road to healing. A thought-provoking and interesting read of the author's personal story, including her extraordinary introspective insight as well as practical advice for personal healing. I can personally relate to much of what is shared in this book, having experienced several revelations while reading, bringing clarity to my own healing path. It is an educational and inspiring story for anyone who is in search of alignment and healing in their own life. I highly recommend this book!
—Jennifer Estrada, Life & Spiritual Coach-Life Purpose Institute, Marconic Energy Practitioner

Align Your Body
Align Your Life

Quit Bending Over Backwards and Getting Ahead
of Yourself
—Be Well with Inner Alignment—

By LisaBeth Lent

For free playlists and demonstration videos for the IMI method, download the e-guide to create the experience at home at http://www.inneralignmenteducation.com

979-8-9864113-1-6 E-Book

979-8-9864113-0-9 Paperback

Table of Contents

Acknowledgments i

Foreword iii

Introduction vii

Chapter 1: Little "t" Traumas & Dis-ease 1

Chapter 2: The Old Story 21

Chapter 3: Hyper-Independence 53

Chapter 4: Talking the Walk 85

Chapter 5: Getting Schooled 99

Chapter 6: Alignment Lessons 125

Chapter 7: Pause Then Play 147

Chapter 8: Growth Happens 169

Chapter 9: Intuitive Movement 193

Chapter 10: Rewiring & Reprogramming 207

Chapter 11: Trinities of Health 233

Chapter 12: Nutrition: Past, Present & Future............................. 251

Chapter 13: Corporations That Care 265

Chapter 14: Ready or Not..281

Author's Note...291

Resources...293

About the Author..302

Acknowledgments

By not fitting in,
I learned to belong.
By feeling alone,
I found Spirit.
Thank you.

Mitakuye Oyasin. Thank you to all my relations for giving me powerful learning experiences. We are all connected as one human family and I feel it in my bones. I have love in my heart for every single one of you that showed up in my reality to teach me all I needed to know to become the person I am today. Without you, I'd not have the strength to overcome and radiate my truth.

To my parents, you did the best you could with all you knew at the time, coming from your own challenging circumstances and perspective, I love you without condition and with full understanding of life's influences and complexities, now that I am a parent myself and see how legacies are passed from generation to generation. You have gifted me a past worth sharing which many can relate to, in knowing everyone comes from difficult childhood dynamics, and it can be used as their foundation for growth and fuel for healing.

To my daughter, the most significant gift and reflection of my life. You've helped me heal and become the "good enough" role model you deserve and have every right to experience. Thank you for your honesty and authentic expression, I honor you.

To my wing man and hero, you challenge my ego, heal my soul, and have melted my heart. Thank you.

My Aunt Nancy, who always believed me and in me. I'm eternally grateful for your love and for demonstrating what unconditional love looks and feels like.

To Grandpa Sol, thank you for teaching me about old school rules and the wisdom encased in the story, "Busy the Bus." All he needed was a caring driver to clean him up and put him to good use.

Melissa Drake, my editor and publishing partner, thank you for being my midwife and helping me grow into the next version of myself. Your teamwork, grace, intuition, and compassion gave me the strength and trust needed to create this book. Thank you for your impeccable guidance, honesty, presence, and intuitive inspiration.

Amanda Flaker, your "downloads" always sync with and validate my intuition. Through the years, your perspective of the bigger picture and the Win-Win-Win of the Abundance Matrix supported my innate conviction that we foster a new future with our radiant beingness and know we are the change we've been waiting for.

I'm grateful for the insights of Gabor Maté, Lisa A Romano, Bitten Johnson, Joe Dispenza, Kyle Cease, Mark Farley, Esther Hicks, Oprah Winfrey, Eckart Tolle, Brené Brown, Shawn Baker, Dr. Lisa Weiderman and so many others for being pioneers of the next paradigm of wellness. On with the evolution.

Foreword

When LisaBeth came to me for help to publish this book, I was excited and intrigued by her story. To say her message aligned with my own story is an understatement. The details and circumstances are different, of course, but the underlying message of being an empath and learning to recognize, own, and honor one's truth despite not being shown the way or supported in that endeavor, is a universal message many have experienced. Throw in a few uncomfortable and vulnerable truths, a spiritual awakening or two, a few dark nights of the soul, and deep empathy for the journey of discovery, and it's a recipe for surviving the human experience.

I never consider the timing of a book's message a coincidence and Align Your Body, Align Your Life is no different.

As we collaborated to bring this book to life, both LisaBeth and I experienced significant expansion in our lives. The deeper we went to develop the book's content, the deeper transformation that occurred for both of us. The process of bringing the book to life was an exercise in trust. It was a literal dance between acknowledging needs, honoring desires, and communicating effectively while respecting and balancing one another's interests. It was a process of being seen and held in our imperfections, offering assistance, allowing help, and being supported. All the while, our individual and collective commitment, love, and connection grew. In other words, our interactions were a practice in a deeper embodiment of the book's message. Her intuitive and integrative movement method helped to solidify and integrate the changes we made along the way.

I pray that you see yourself in these pages and have the opportunity to experience the same embodiment I did while working with LisaBeth's story—that is, the ability to get present and quit bending over backward and getting ahead of yourself so you can be well with inner alignment.

—Melissa Drake, LisaBeth's publishing partner and author of *The Orgasmic Entrepreneur* and *TranscenDANCE*

If you want to become whole,
let yourself be partial.
If you want to become straight,
let yourself be crooked.
If you want to become full,
let yourself be empty.
If you want to be reborn,
let yourself die.
If you want to be given everything,
give everything up.

The Master, by residing in the Tao,
sets an example for all beings.
Because he doesn't display himself,
people can see his light.
Because he has nothing to prove,
people can trust his words.
Because he doesn't know who he is,
people recognize themselves in him.
Because he has no goal in mind,
everything he does succeeds.

When the ancient Masters said,
"If you want to be given everything,
give everything up,"
They weren't using empty phrases.
Only in being lived by the Tao
can you be truly yourself.

22, Tao Te Ching, A new English version by Stephen Mitchell

Introduction

Let Me Clear My Throat

"Those who cannot remember the past are condemned to repeat it."
– George Santayana, The Life of Reason, 1905

Being human gives each person legitimacy and automatically marks the inherent worth of us all. There's nothing to prove. We are valuable just for existing. Feeling worthy depends on perspective and circumstance, but being worthy—that's a birthright. From the moment babies are born, and regardless of how imperfect their human form may be, ALL are perfectly lovable as they are. For many like myself, the human journey quickly goes downhill from there. Somehow, we never forget that state of immaculate purity we once were in, and some want to return to that place of unconditional, accepting love. Returning to that level of wellness is a journey riddled with paradoxes. Wellness actually lives only in the present moment; the future unfolds from it, while the past creates a collection of memories and their associated beliefs. The most profound of contradictory and complementary phenomena is how the journey to wholeness is a solitary adventure one cannot do alone.

Learning from our past and what made us who we are is the only way to move forward in the freedom of it. Without reflection, our history holds us captive. Ignoring it keeps us chained to past patterns and from true health since few of us learned how to be healthy and well in our upbringing.

The sum of our body, mind, and emotions determines our health. Where we struggle is in our blind spots, where we deny our struggle is where we have "dis-ease." Breaking up this word for effect, as illness is the lack of effortless functioning, the absence of ease. Curiosity is the path of the antidote to dis-ease; taking on brave discovery to the root cause of sickness instead of glossing over the symptoms with medication. Treating an ailment is simple, not easy, given that appropriate treatment is the focus, not just covering it up or numbing it.

To cure an illness, first, we have to reveal the sources. There is no emPOWERment with numbing the messages our bodies send. Pharmaceutical businesses have no interest in that. They make money by managing symptoms, not curing dis-eases. That is why it's so hard to get many doctors to investigate and uncover the root cause. Rather than truly restore health, they are encouraged to write prescriptions. As a result, the "cure" is never found or realized, ending in the long-term management of symptoms until death or until the patient discovers a path to become well. Unwell folks cycle the same malady while increasing prescription drugs causing new symptoms that require additional medications. This is the means to their end unless they come to believe there is another way beyond the widely accepted one of traditional medicine.

Victimhood and feeling defeated is an illness and all too common nowadays. People wear their complaints as badges of honor and proud barriers to wellness. Their limiting beliefs keep them unwell, and they can't imagine life without their problems. Like those who learned victim mentality as part of their initiation to life, disemPOWERment was my first dis-ease that led to all the others. That orientation took me into the land of confusion and banished me there until I came to the honesty to acknowledge it, which took years to sort out. All the other illnesses I suffered were rooted in my disemPOWERment, and I describe how they are related throughout this book.

In the paradox of surrender, I discovered the way to win.

This is a book of wellness, how I became well after a lifetime of being emotionally, physically, and mentally "off." Here, I share my life's healing story as an example of what restoring the birthright of healthfulness looks and feels like. My story is a guide of sorts, an offering to how you can find your own unique way to your own health restoration. My story is anyone's story. It's both individual and a collective story. Being human ain't no walk in the park; anyone who depicts it differently is a liar or self-deceived. Without real suffering, there can be no real joy.

My first sickness was that of powerlessness. I had intermittent confidence depending on how intimidated I was by others in the room. Boundaries were not taught; they were only disregarded, which caused me many relating problems. As a result, codependency became my first coping mechanism in adapting to dysfunctional family dynamics. Before I was ten, panic, guilt, shame, and resentment were everyday emotions running, unbeknownst to me. No one, especially myself, recognized them. Accepting the defeat of neglect creates a default of minimization of self. And so it went, dysfunction begets more dysfunction, and socially-acceptable addictions beget more socially-acceptable addictions. Avoidance and numbing out became my go-tos for dealing with what was too much for me to handle. Self-pity and sweets were the first methods used to deal with my frustrating and less-than-ideal circumstances.

The second dis-ease, a symptom of the first, was self-neglect, a natural outcome of my childhood neglect. After many failed attempts to get my needs met, the disappointment and shame that went along with it, wore me out. It was futile to keep trying, so I learned to back off, and geographically go all over. I learned how to minimize and bypass my needs and preferences despite myself. There were many far-reaching consequences, which are shared in this book's first section. The ultimate outcome, though, was the path of restoring what was lost, my innate value, unlearning self-neglect by listening within.

Although my path is different, I'm not alone in the experience of self-neglect. Based on my observations and interactions with others, I'd say I share the company of a good portion of the human population. To sum it up, consistently experiencing invalidation and minimization in childhood, we internalize the reactions of others in these ways:

We were ignored; we ignored ourselves.

We were invalidated; we invalidated ourselves.

We were criticized; we criticized ourselves.

And just like that, we became small. Subordinate codependency is born from the socially accepted and familiar dynamic of internalizing the emotional marginalization received from those closest to us.

Self-neglect gets old and outdated. We start to look for a way out and begin to care more for our health and wellness. We can connect the unhealthy ways of relating to our personal dysfunction in health and the health of the culture overall. An emotional intelligence rEvolution dawning extends to business culture and society at large, welcoming absolute accountability of health and whole wellness. This next renaissance is one of awareness, stopping the train of busyness, emotional neglect, and all the convenient distractions that wreck our well-being.

Think of the upcoming chapters as hacks for getting your shit together and aligning with a life that feels good to you. Remember, there is no birth without labor. There is no success without some kind of pain and discomfort. There will be no woo-woo, overly optimistic spiritual bantering here. There will be anecdotes, observations, and strategies to increase confidence and contentment in your life.

There is an alignment process to emPOWERment via self-preservation to cure disemPOWERment and self-neglect. Alignment happens as a natural outcome of migrating from powerlessness to preservation. It begins with a decision to care, claiming self as a priority. It is accomplished by leaning into non-judgmental awareness and moving away from numbing out, ruminating, and worshiping distractions.

What is alignment?

It's like refinement, but it has an element of balance. To be aligned is to be harmonized. The science of ergonomics is for our physical alignment, and the environment is shaped to support our healthy alignment to maximize efficiency. I use ergonomics as a tool for inner alignment in the corporate world instead of selling office furniture. The awareness that ergonomics brings to a person can be used as a gateway to a better understanding of the body's inner workings. My work in the corporate environment came from the direct experience of working on having better posture and body mechanics and less chronic muscular pain (more on that later). I used my story as an example of what inner alignment looks and feels like. Getting one's body in line and in balance is akin to any masterpiece. First the dream, then the draft, then the details. It's a labor of love. Love is action, often including friction.

Heat and pressure make diamonds. They also make strong, valuable people. Alignment matters because we desire it because we sense it to be important in our existence. Getting into alignment is a pursuit of self-care, not self-indulgence. It's not luxurious or extraneous. Taking leadership of our own lives is our choice, as painful as it is at first, to disappoint others by not doing what they want with our lives. Alignment is claiming our sovereignty and our integrity while owning the trajectory of our lives.

In aligning to our values and priorities, our awareness depends on the things and people we care about. What is it we want? What are our personal preferences? Values get obscured when we are immersed in our convenient, addictive escape mechanisms, numbing and perpetuating our habituated negligence. If one wants to escape any form of pain, there are plenty of options. Our maladaptive and addictive coping mechanisms block our alignment. I've tried hard to bypass this myself; it is futile. Our means of distraction and avoidance can be insidiously deceptive! Sidestepping the blocks preventing us from true and sustainable alignment cannot work. Alignment to our own joyous, authentic life cannot materialize without addressing and eliminating our blockages to emBODYment, i.e., maladaptive coping mechanisms. Yes, there will always be aversions because we are human. We will just handle them differently as we progress towards achieving alignment.

What blocks emBODYment? Avoidance. It comes in many forms and is the great barricade. It's not only found in extreme hard drugs but subtle and frequently abused everyday vices. Often viewed as harmless, some of the most popular examples sabotage our sovereignty and internal power: caffeine, nicotine, alcohol, social media, overeating, overspending, over-screening, over-sexing, and staying high all the live-long day with cannabis. Underneath all that distraction and avoidance lie our true feelings and opinions about how life is and how it is managed.

Instead of navigating a world of "have tos" and "shoulds," which represent misalignment, there lies a world of freedom and acceptance. Imagine always showing up exactly as you are, knowing you are accepted by yourself first and foremost and then by those you love, being free to feel your feelings in every given moment of all your days forevermore.

I bet you're wondering if that's even possible. There's no need to have a complete overhaul of any kind, but to accept your life as it is, only feeling healthy, balanced, and at peace with all of its dimensions. Imagine, living your life as you prefer instead of becoming the person others expect you to be. Tapping into the body makes it so.

The method of alignment I created was originally designed for people who are disconnected from their bodies, hate to exercise (like I did), and are longing to actually enjoy physical activity (instead of a form of punishment). The Intuitive Movement Integration (IMI) experience is multi-faceted and has far-reaching benefits. It is a strategy for physical health, but also for stress reduction, personal emBODYment, and inner emPOWERment. It also proves to be a useful team-builder in organizations as an emotional intelligence development tool and an effective way to enhance non-verbal communication, confidence, and leadership skills.

The light-hearted, enjoyable group dynamic builds trust, healthy boundaries, and psychological safety within a team construct. As practiced, IMI is the physical shortcut to grasp most of the points made in this book somatically. Confidence and body acceptance are learned and reinforced through posture awareness and improvement. It relieves social anxiety immeasurably by cultivating emotional awareness among a group with playfulness. IMI was designed and intended for low-energy people, but the method is useful for anyone. People get out of it exactly what they need. That's the magic of it.

The IMI method taught me how emotional awareness and internal focus are at the epicenter of our innate power. It is the practice of self-prioritization; you, as the most important person to yourself, so that everyone else gets what they need from you, always in that order. Were you conditioned to care first for others' emotions while ignoring your own? Maybe you're in the habit of negating your feelings and pacifying your preferences so that you don't cause a fuss. Does having needs make you feel like being you is a bother and to be avoided at all costs? With practice, it doesn't have to be anymore. Designing a new pattern, acknowledging and responsibly communicating your feelings and preferences is anything but selfish. It is self-preservation. It's your life and your focus. There need no guilt, no shame, no fear. Imagine that. I believe it can be done because I've done it. Now I share it so that it may spark the belief that mental, emotional, and physical wellness is possible for you.

There will be little talk about the codependent-narcissistic phenomenon because there's no solution to that. Codependency will be discussed but in the context of ownership. There is no narcissist to blame once we recognize our own victim role. We all play our part in the drama of unhealthy relationships.

The core of this book is designed to assist in upgrading old unhealthy beliefs and behaviors for fresh new ones that benefit our whole being. Using my own personal details and insights as examples and sharing some simple practices, I'll demonstrate how to take the focus off of others and shine the light on how to train and center our attention on ourselves to extract the lessons contained in life's interactions. Our health and wellness deserve no less.

Yes, really. We are deserving of our own prioritization and to benefit from what happened to us "back then."

In my obsession to reflect on things, education became a habit and expanded my understanding of people, perspective, and history. Psychology and philosophy gave great insight into solving the riddle of my chronically unhappy, unsatisfying life. The context brought understanding, and humility delivered breakthroughs. Without understanding all the parts of the past, the future becomes a replication of it. Everything unevaluated and unaddressed is repeated. By recognizing patterns of thought and action, we open up to another way and a new space to explore. Unlearning and new learning defines our growth away from habits that harm into habits that help. Growth is consciousness in action.

Consciousness breaks the chains of living a life on autopilot. Awareness is often synonymous with "perception," but it's more than mere perspective, it's a wider angle, a bigger picture. Perception is only one angle, where awareness captures many (although there will be blind spots, which is why we need others' awareness to help us out at times). Undesirable, outdated habits live in the land of limited perception; liberation from them emerges from an expanded awareness.

Like any human, I take liberties that others condemn and judge as wrong. I say things people are too scared to say. I live messily and have failed frequently. In this book, I share authentically and imperfectly. How dare I? I dare speak my truth the best I know how—what absolute gumption. Who do I think I am? Well, me. And from the real me, I say exactly what I need to say. Rebelliousness has one of my signature traits, dodging convention for its lack of creativity. It got me in tons of trouble as a kid and continues to perplex people who play by the old rules.

This book exemplifies the restoration process—revitalizing what once was there, removing what can now be removed, and putting everything where it belongs again. We are born naturally honest, confident, and expressive. We were joyous, loving, full of wonder, and unconditionally loving. Recovering these natural states of being is the reclamation of our innate power instead of continuing the fear of it. We can discover and get past the fear of our own power by allowing the honesty of vulnerable humility—even if we've only experienced poor examples of it in our past. The way we relate to power influences how we relate to our inner experience. We may feel like a different person as we restore the power once removed with the indoctrination of social conformity in lieu of true belonging. When control returns to us, we will never feel more ourselves: a welcomed change, our birthright, this state of sovereignty. There is no shame in what was because it all leads us to exactly where we need to be to reach our goals. This book will demonstrate how it's done.

EmBODYment means to know your truth and live it. It's a matter of walking the talk. To be transparent, I talked a lot. But, I wasn't walking in line with my beliefs until my awareness showed me vital blind spots and strongholds that needed revelations to live in the integrity of my own advice. I had to be rejected for my truth initially to learn its impact. For many like myself, before power is disemPOWERment, before acceptance is rejection. As I have learned, this book was created for emPOWERment, helping others claim their sovereignty and dignity without compromise.

Now is the right time. Better late than never.

I encourage you to courageously dive into a better understanding of yourself through my stories, insights, and exercises. This work will resonate with many, trigger most, and piss off a few. Explore whoever you want to be and do whatever you want to do, so long as you're not hurting anyone else in the process. Yes, I promise you will disappoint some as part of the restoration process. That's inevitable when you're following your inner guidance and becoming the leader of your own life.

Sharing all I am aware of to get my message of hope and health conveyed, I hope this is useful and inspiring in your journey towards attaining whole well-being through emBODYment and emPOWERment for you, your team, and humanity. A lofty desire, but hey, a girl can dream, right?

Trust the process. Take your time with each chapter, do not rush the process if you find yourself needing to "chew" on the ideas and exercises suggested. If you decide to partake in the challenges at the end of certain chapters, pause your reading until you complete them. Fellow traveler, I wish you pure, unconditional love of the most divine variety all your way.

1

*"The question is not why the addiction,
but why the pain."*

- Gabor Maté

Chapter 1

Little "t" Traumas & Dis-ease

"It is no measure of health to be well adjusted
to a profoundly sick society."
—Jiddu Krishna murti

Getting well in a sick culture is a task of no small measure. Our state of unwellness is reflected in the abundance of dysfunctional relationships that are deemed "normal." Normal is far from well. If the sick are convinced they are healthy, then the healthy appear to be sick. Mental and emotional health has been crying out for attention and only recently began getting the love it needs. Priorities only shift when people hit their bottom. Well, the base all but fell out of our rock bottom. Amirite?

Shedding light on how mental and emotional health tie into physical health is vital to understanding the roadblocks to being healthy and well. First, we have to gain awareness by acknowledging them. Making it no big deal to speak about such topics removes the negative connotations of mental and emotional well-being issues. This book provides real talk for real people who have real problems, like everyone else—the only requirement is honesty. Instead of pretending we're all fine and dandy, it's ok—even courageous—to admit we are far from dandy and stop pretending.

Being born has only one implied promise—others will meet your needs, love, and care for you. For many, like myself, the families we were born into didn't exactly fulfill the promise. Our first newborn cries of frustration and disappointment were often met with some kind of betrayal (a separation, aka, an attachment wound). Our caregivers responded with intense anger, hostile frustration, guilt-ridden neglect, and sometimes blatant abandonment. That first betrayal (or trauma) caused a sequenced ripple effect, establishing and solidifying our personality and creating a specific relational orientation towards our caregivers and the rest of the world. Our attachment type, the way we relate to others, originated in these early stages of infant development. This initiation into the three-dimensional world created the first internal distress, our first neglect, our first abuse, and our first dissonant confusion. These sensations were quickly followed by the first suppression of emotional discomfort resulting from these clashing of needs and preferences with our caregivers. The birth of trauma begins for us all at this juncture. Disconnection breaks our hearts and leaves a trail of wounds only for the process of maturity to soothe them. Maturity is not inevitable, tragically, as we can plainly see in ourselves and others. However, little "t" traumas are unavoidable.

Little "t" traumas for all

Big T and little "t" traumas set the trajectory of our life's experiences. Big T traumas are the sudden accidents and huge events that seem to fall upon us without warning or much preparation. The cruel, gruesome events can and often make us question the meaning of our existence. PTSD is usually the effect of big T traumatic events. Little "t" traumas are insidious, causing rifts in bonds and eroding our ability to trust. Attachment trauma begins at the very beginning of our adventure of this incarnation and continues to engrain the programming of how we view the world and how we relate to it. Our conditioned beliefs cannot shift until we realize the patterns and instigate the desire to interrupt them. The way we were parented and life itself create tiny micro-tears and gaping holes in the fabric of effortless trust. And just like that, the world becomes skewed by our painful experiences. Only those who decide they can no longer continue with their pain can fathom the notion of stopping it. The maturity process continually initiates growth, completing old patterns and kicking off new ones. Utterly unrelated to one's age, maturity is alertness and awareness. It has everything to do with an honest assessment of evolving needs, desires, and actions. Mature people have hope that life can change for the better. The wise are self-accountable. They are not victims of circumstance. The mature-minded earn their growth by embracing the pain of life, transmuting it into the origin of their fulfillment. Simple, but rarely easy, emBODYing acceptance is the way to wisdom and development. Conceptualizing acceptance is a phenomenon beyond words.

Before we knew the language of words, emotion was our first innate language. After understanding, speaking, and learning words, the language of others often begins to override, ignore, and invalidate our emotions for the sake of control. We learned to please our caregivers, appeasing them to avoid feelings of anger, shame, guilt, and fear. To quell our discontent, we learned to be distracted by pacifiers, bottles, food, toys, screens, and other ploys to dismiss and avoid acknowledging our emotional responses to our experiences. This grooming for addictive escape was cultivated right there through the demands of our caregivers. "Don't cry." "Shut up." "Stop being so sensitive." And my favorite, "Get over it," shouted amid a temper tantrum, we are redirected to look at something else and feel happy instead of being given the space to feel and work out less than desirable feelings like anger, frustration, annoyance, confusion, and grief.

The messages to deny our emotions are consistent in many people's upbringing. Maladaptive coping mechanisms (the most common are substance abuse, rumination, emotional numbing, and escape) swoop in, giving us a way to adapt to the external denial of our emotional realities. Addictive personalities are formed in response to personal pains and traumas, both big and small. Bestselling author, renowned speaker, and addiction specialist, Gabor Maté has this to say about the relationship between pain, trauma, and addictive patterns:

> Not all addictions are rooted in abuse or trauma, but I do believe they can all be traced to painful experiences. A hurt is at the center of all addictive behaviors. It is present in the gambler, the Internet addict, the compulsive shopper, and

the workaholic. The wound may not be as deep and the ache not as excruciating, and it may even be entirely hidden—but it's there.

Due to pain and trauma, driving into unhealthy substances and behaviors becomes a standard coping mechanism. It's instinctive protection formulated by resistance and negligence of our thoughts and feelings by our custodians. The need for approval and fear of abandonment is embedded deeply in our DNA and prevents us from disconnecting completely. Humans are social animals, and our survival is dependent upon others. As individuals, we cannot thrive in a vacuum, no matter how we try.

How dis-ease begins

This "acting out," i.e., using maladaptive coping mechanisms to deal with others' resistance to our true feelings, spins the wheels of avoidance, distraction, and self-victimization. The ignored energy and emotion have to go someplace. Since it cannot be expressed to others, it gets expressed inside, wreaking havoc in our bodies, hearts, and minds. That internal strife becomes the current through which our energy flows. Thus, avoidance of the underlying emotions sets the stage for ongoing unhealthy relating and going to self-destructive addictions of many kinds.

Avoiding pain and seeking pleasure are fundamental aspects of being human. Escape is simple and easy for so many—until we learn that there's no avoiding the pain of being human. To be human is to suffer. Life presents unlimited discomforts. The challenge and beauty are to find meaning and grow with the pain. Too many never find the way out of numbing out and self-neglect.

The accountability factor is the magic ingredient to a life filled with joy, happiness, and freedom.

The only way out is through. Maturation is getting beyond the dysfunctional coping mechanisms, moving forward with honest, healthy relating, and starting with our conversations with ourselves.

The way of ease begins where you are

We have to acknowledge our active role in unhealthy patterning with brave insight. Getting well is a process of identifying and removing obstructing factors and replacing these blockages with health-benefiting components. In Chinese medicine, the obstructions are referred to as "insults" (more about that in Chapter 5). Wanting to overcome addictions and avoidant behaviors means confronting the emotional cycles of guilt, remorse, and disappointment. Unhealthy habits, addictions, and avoidances actually reinforce these difficult emotions. When we're sick of the feelings associated with being unhealthy, we can begin to envision the possibility of a better life. There is no restoration of wellness without a sliver of hope for a better way to live.

Most people use their resentments of other people's actions and personal health issues to perpetuate unhappiness and dissatisfaction, not realizing that most health and relationships reside in their control. In fact, no one else has the power to dictate our health and the way we relate to others. The path to wellness (personal and social) requires introspection, patience, and a gentle understanding of the circumstances at play. There are layers of dynamic responses and intended actions running under the surface. Everyone has their own angle to justify their own perception, so considering other perspectives can bring understanding and acceptance. Accepting responsibility for our own reactions is the mark of budding maturity.

New actions replace old ones, and the desire to replace them is the root of ending addictions, but it's not as easy as substituting one thing for another. The root of addiction must be addressed, or another destructive addiction will replace the old one. The thoughts and feelings fueling the addiction need to be seen and understood to process them, so the maladaptive coping mechanism is obsolete. This introspection is delicate because it is easily clouded by projection. Projection is a blame game, a hall of mirrors that shifts the ownership away from our behavior and blames others for our actions. Staying focused on our feelings guides the process of looking within. Context is useful, so it can be good to label others to help draw boundaries between them and us. The labels become a step along the way to healing. The language of healing relationships is akin to any other study. Codependency and narcissism are useful labels for context. Still, most folks are a bit of both (the codependent has narcissistic traits, and the narcissist has codependent traits) until they are fully restored to wellness. I only have a few more words to speak to the language of unhealthy relating, i.e., the codependency-narcissism spectrum.

They are two sides of the same dirty coin. People who lean towards narcissism use empathy against others, while codependents use empathy against themselves. Both sorts of people are conflicted and relate manipulatively, however subconsciously. Both fixate on one person (the narcissist) and dodge self-responsibility in blaming the other for their circumstances. Both have direct responsibility in their relational circumstances. Only codependents can validate their suffering with a wider lens of the unhealthy dynamic because they are often willing to admit fault, so they are the ones who typically venture for solutions. Narcissists cannot have a wider lens because they are committed to their "correct" perspective and unwilling to acknowledge solutions exist. The general relationship between narcissism and codependency is a tool for helping us to identify our responsibility in our unhealthy relating. I'm not speaking about clinical personality disorders here. Context is for clarity, allowing us to see where we stand in dynamics. Labels are purely egoic, and we are more than our egos. Because egos dictate our reactions, we need to see it for its intended purpose. The ego is not bad or good. It serves to protect us.

Welcome ego and higher consciousness

The ego is only something to be aware of, not something to overcome. It's vital to recognize the ego as a built-in protection mechanism and not try to condemn or erase it. The ego presents perpetual compulsions of specific behaviors in response to familiar circumstances. The ego functions to reference memories and gauge an appropriate (and safe) reaction. It is not conscious. Below consciousness, the ego lives in the subconscious mind. We dialogue between the ego and our "higher self" as the devil and angel who figuratively exist on our left and right shoulders. One serves instant gratification while the other serves the greater good and plays the long game. The chatter among these two characters is one of the most important conversations to tune into. Some liken our consciousness to God-consciousness, and I agree. Still, it is not essential to believe that your higher consciousness, the aspect that knows what is truly best for your health and well-being, is a spiritual higher power influencing you. While the ego fears, the greater consciousness loves. There is a need for both in us. The ego gives us context and illuminates our records and old beliefs, witnesses our beliefs, and observes the patterns. Question the ego's priorities and compulsions to disrupt the old patterns, ending them in order to begin a new routine. Greater consciousness develops new solutions to repetitive problems where they can be left in the past, and we can move forward in a harmonious way.

Your ego is not the enemy when it comes to the pursuit of wholeness. Ego is an individualistic necessity that differentiates people. Humans are made the same. We have the same bones, blood, and guts among our different traits. Cultural backgrounds dictate the diversity in our headspace, and the various realities radiate out from there. Finding our purpose lies in the conversation between the ego and greater consciousness—for those fortunate and brave enough to start the dialogue. The curiosity of discovering one's life's purpose leads to alignment, and there's nothing woo-woo about it. Alignment is self-actualization, and acceptance of all that was is its foundation.

The business of misery

Much akin to the alignment of our spinal column, something is off when we're not aligned. We feel out of whack; we feel constant pain and discomfort. Aligning to our truest priorities and purpose gives life meaning, quality, and satisfaction. Sadly, more people are focused on surviving than thriving. Creating a life of purpose seems like a dream only the entitled can conceive. It turns out that those who dare delve into exploring their purpose seem to make the opportunities to do so. The pain is too great to remain the same, locked into a life that is unsatisfying. How many folks do you know going through the motions of being alive who seem to be a shell that's empty inside? How many people are on psych drugs now for depression and other mood disturbances? The statistics are alarming. According to the Centers for Disease Control, 13.2% of adults in the USA used antidepressants between 2015 and 2018.[1] That's more than one out of every ten adults. Worse, the usage significantly increases with age.

How many seemingly random (and not so random) suicides have taken your loved ones and friends? Suicide is the fourth leading cause of death for 15–19-year-olds, and there are over 700,000 suicides worldwide every year, according to the World Health Organization 2021.[2] Painkillers and mood inhibitors have been among the top forty most widely prescribed pharmaceuticals year after year.[3] In 2019, 9.7 million people misused prescription pain relievers in the US alone.[4]

The one thing those going through the motions have in common is an inner emptiness or deep pain that won't let up. There's a missing piece in their lives, and they feel it. That is what it is to be misaligned with their purpose, fueling an escape from the life they were given with all other things to substitute a sensation of

---

[1] https://www.cdc.gov/nchs/products/databriefs/db377.htm
[2] https://www.who.int/news-room/fact-sheets/detail/suicide
[3] https://www.healthgrades.com/right-care/patient-advocate/the-top-50-drugs-prescribed-in-the-united-states
[4] https://www.hhs.gov/opioids/about-the-epidemic/opioid-crisis-statistics

wholeness and peace. Purpose, by the way, does not need to be some huge endeavor like a new business or a dramatic shift in one's circumstances. Finding our purpose can mean small adjustments to the way we relate to life and all that it is comprised of. Small shifts in how we communicate have big effects on our realities. Quick fixes like numbing out or short-term avoidances merely delay or amplify the problem.

Pills attempt to fix symptoms while concealing emotional pain

Taking pills to fix the pain is like using duct tape to fix a broken car part. It might work for a while, but the part is still broken and eventually needs to be addressed before matters get worse or the car gets junked. The root cause still lingers no matter what medications are taken to alleviate the symptoms of the pain and discomfort. People who suffer from the effects of little and big traumas of unprocessed chronic mental, emotional, and physical pain experience a continual frustration with life as it is versus how they feel it "should" be. The conflict of living in consistent denial of how they desire to live depletes the will to thrive. Eventually, they wear down and out. People wallow in disappointment, in complete disbelief that life can have less pain and anguish and more pleasure and relief. People have learned hopelessness based on the cultural norms of the mainstream narrative that suffering is endless and living with it "is what it is." Too many are self-defeated. All hope for living a life of satisfaction and fulfillment is lost. Based on a sense of deprivation and denial planted in childhood and reinforced in cultural expectations, limiting beliefs are passed through the generations from our parents, their parents, and their parents.

Believing alignment is possible

To truly create this idea of a "good" and satisfying life requires unlearning all the limitations we grew to become comfortable with. So, how does one unlearn the constant narrative that keeps them stuck in dissatisfaction? By asking essential questions, un-learning and re-programing is a natural outgrowth. Some common questions to get started include the following:

- What are our beliefs about what life is "supposed" to be and look like?

- What do we care about?

- What topics excite us?

- What limiting beliefs were we taught as children?

Over time, our lives are programmed by things we see in the environment. We learn what girls and boys do, how to get ahead in the office, and how class-specific trades and educations box us in. Questioning these original observations and beliefs begins the process of unlearning. Being crazy enough to be interested in something despite it revolting others is courageous. When shut down from going a different way from the pack, we shied away from our goals, hopes, and desires for so many reasons—most related to the expected judgments of others. Ask the questions. It's a little like the toothpaste analogy; once you ask, you can't un-ask the question, and the answer is out there. You've exposed it. Once the toothpaste is out of the tube, you can't put it back. Instead, you clean up the sticky mess by finding answers to your existence. Once we connect to our passions, life becomes a journey of adventure, anything but lifeless.

The process of alignment is challenging. The world may seem largely disinterested, indifferent, or even offended by our individual path to health, wellness, and purposeful life. Significant obstacles to alignment exist that can feel surreal. It's a training ground, necessary steps along the way. Stumbling blocks are fuel for the fire. We are the fire, the wrought iron, being strengthened by the intense heat and hammering of life. The process of alignment goes exactly this way for good reason. It weeds out the ones who only want the easy way. Nothing worthwhile is without some effort.

Many valid roadblocks seem to block us, and that stops many from moving forward while others find a way up, over, or through it. What is different between these two different groups of people? Some make themselves matter, and others do not. It's their values and priorities. To each their own; one is not better than another. Other values are more important than the pursuit of their own alignment, which is ok for them. People who prioritize their desires feel they matter as much, if not more than other priorities in their worlds, that's why. When we know we matter, and what we feel matters, our needs and wants can be met. So, if anyone desires to, they can learn to matter more and make their feelings, needs, and wants matter too.

Matters of mattering

If we don't give precedence to what matters (like people, passions, and priorities), they fall out of focus, and what doesn't really matter can seem to be more important. Matter is physical in the scientific sense but also conceptual in a theoretical sense. I know this modern-day trigger word, "matter," has many meanings and is a touchy subject. The social associations of this word can hip-chuck any well-meaning person into the paradoxical and chaotic world of politics. Here it is, and its definition according to (who else) Google:

mat·ter

/ˈmadər/

noun

physical substance in general, as distinct from mind and spirit; (in physics) that which occupies space and possesses rest mass, especially as distinct from energy.

"the structure and properties of matter"

an affair or situation under consideration; a topic.

"a great deal of work was done on this matter"

verb

be of importance; have significance.

"it doesn't matter what the guests wear"

(of a wound) secrete or discharge pus.

Ok, that last verb reference is pretty gross, but see how powerful this simple word is? Even by definition, matter is highly contextual. It's significant physically and conceptually. What matters? Do you matter to you? Do your opinions and feelings matter to you?

To every one of us, some things matter, and others don't. Yet, matter has literal and figurative weight, it has value. Matter takes priority. *Things that matter guide our preferences and priorities.* When matter is unimportant, it is not seen. It has no value or function.

When things and people don't matter, they are devalued and dehumanized. That's where humans get both serious and funny (not in a good way, funny).

How we determine what matters has everything to do with our perspective, values, and priorities. What matters is relational, vibrational, and unique to us. Maybe that's precisely what Einstein was referring to when he said, "Concerning matter, we have been all wrong. What we have called matter is energy, whose vibration has been so lowered as to be perceptible to the senses. There is no matter." If that's true (and I really trust Einstein when it comes to this topic), there's only energy behind matter, and that energy is INTENT. What lies behind our priorities are the intentions, whether aware of them or not. Our intent is revealed in what we say and do in response to what matters to us.

From unstable to aligned

The pressure to accommodate and harmonize with our family, peers, and society is immense in childhood and adolescence. Being conditioned to go along with the status quo, we often repress our instincts when it goes against the grain of others, which blocks our intuitive expression. Others unknowingly can project what they believe we should be, do, and speak. So many of us are expected to be more emotionally mature than developmentally appropriate, usually, around the time we start walking. The race to become independent and self-sufficient doesn't let up until we have a breakdown or two. When breaking down, we learn how to fall apart so we can put ourselves back together with new parts and in new ways. With the breaking down, we break**through** into the following stages of growth. As challenging as they can be, *there's no breakthrough when there's no breakdown.*

Without a breakdown, the status quo is maintained. Without honestly questioning "What's it all for?" we get desensitized to that nagging sensation of something amiss in our day-to-day rigid routines, using outdated coping mechanisms to keep chugging on. Breaking things apart is required to put them together in a new way. Growth is not for everyone; some folks are meant to stay fixed as they are. I say, "More power to them." I honor their choice and understand everyone doesn't need to grow and mature. Each person is sovereign and chooses their path. Some people are designed to grow, while others are meant to uphold the status quo. We need both, and the decision is up to each individual. Eventually, the status quo gradually shifts, slowly over time. The best growth is incremental, as slow growth has the most staying power. The methods and approaches I suggest are based on an unrushed, gradual awareness away from dis-ease and toward sustainably restoring health and well-being.

Humans need the status quo, and stability is a practical and logical need. Tony Robbins has preached many times about his six human needs:[5]

1. Certainty: assurance you can avoid pain and gain pleasure
2. Uncertainty/Variety: the need for the unknown, change, new stimuli
3. Significance: feeling unique, important, special or needed

---

[5] https://www.tonyrobbins.com/mind-meaning/do-you-need-to-feel-significant/

4. Connection/Love: a strong feeling of closeness or union with someone or something

5. Growth: an expansion of capacity, capability or understanding

6. Contribution: a sense of service and focus on helping, giving to and supporting others

Balance is the key to life, right? Humans need certainty, but we also need an element of variety, or we die of boredom and its related symptoms (stimulating diversions of our boring lives). I set out to get used to change early on and in hindsight I've learned change and novelty can be hard on the body. Change takes some energy, it's an investment with a price tag equal to the risks and losses of old ways of being. Expanded awareness is worth every bold decision, from my vantage point.

Our backstory reveals how our needs and values came to be and helps us recognize what we prefer for our future. Using our personal history as a tool for context brings on our next breakthrough. If you're lucky, you'll have more than a few throughout your lifetime.

Stillness in Action

List your inventory of coping mechanisms:

- ✓ What do you do to cope when something doesn't go your way?

- ✓ What activities make you feel more comfortable during tense situations?

- ✓ What do you waste time on when you "should" be doing something else?

- ✓ What is life "supposed" to look like to you?

List an inventory of your values:

- ✓ What do you care about most?

- ✓ What topics interest you?

- ✓ What would you want for this world if you could make it exactly as you wish?

Action in Stillness

- ✓ Sit or walk and contemplate your values, hopes, and dreams for your life and their perceived obstacles. Identify the beliefs associated with each.

- ✓ Use your five senses of smell, taste, touch, see, and hear, while observing your surroundings and take a few deep breaths.

- ✓ Notice what thoughts come up and identify the judgments associated with those thoughts.

2

Truth hurts.
Happy pharma pills
to skirt the issue.
Less for me.
Pain is evidence.
Follow the clues.

Poetry Piece from "Connection"

Chapter 2

The Old Story

"Once upon a time, a tiny striped caterpillar burst from the egg which had been home for so long. "Hello world," he said.
—Trina Paulus, Hope for the Flowers

In utero and beyond

I was born into a bit of a romantic drama. I was one of those babies conceived to save a broken marriage. My father was having an affair with his secretary when I was in my momma's belly. My mother was heartbroken while I was in her womb and for most of my young life. They got back together until my mom committed retaliatory adultery to get back at him. The backstory of my parent's failed relationship was well known to me. My father regularly shared the juicy details of their tumultuous marriage throughout my childhood and adolescence. I was a prime example of an adultified child. Before then, there were many other deviations from a healthy upbringing.

Being born on Christmas Day, my older brother traumatized my mother's desire to have me deliver spontaneously. She had me by appointment, an induction in early August. Never mind that my due date was mid-summer, with ZERO holidays weeks before or after. This one decision may have set the stage for my perpetual frustration, anger, and resentment toward her. I came to believe I was forced to leave the womb against my will rather than arrive into this world when it was my time. I'd be passionately outraged with my poor little five-footed Ma for three more decades for all the reasons I felt were justified. She reminded me repeatedly that she did the best she could under the circumstances. Although I understood, I often felt her remarks were said to negate my feelings about it, which was another insult to injury.

Not being breastfed was another bone of contention. Had I been given the teat, we'd have had a neurological connection. Based on a 10-year study by the American Psychological Association, "Women who breastfeed their children longer exhibit more maternal sensitivity well past the infant and toddler years."[6] Unfortunately, breastfeeding was way too progressive for her, much like many others in 1974.

Another dynamic that set the stage for the chronic disconnection between us could also be my lack of trusting her. The rejection and abandonment issues were set up by the leading authorities of the time. Being a baby abandoned to be put to sleep nightly MAY have influenced my feeling to shut her out rather than turn towards her. That "Crying It Out" method just never sat well with me, and I know this is all hypothesizing here, but I sense that these were nails in

---

[6] https://neurosciencenews.com/breastfeeding-bonding-development-7831/

the coffin setting the trajectory of who I was destined to become and the messy road I had to travel to arrive to become the person I am today. The point is, there's a hell of a lot of evidence around Attachment Theory that states leaving your child to cry themselves to sleep is no bueno. It creates attachment trauma galore!

All the times I felt insignificant and wanted to be seen were ignored and invalidated. Instead of being comforted and loved during those times, my cries were met with annoyance, anger, and denial by her. Of course, this neglect was compounded by my father, who had the same response to my feelings and opinions.

Life didn't go as my mom planned. At 21, her dreams of a perfect marriage (to a 19-year-old kid, mind you) imploded four years later. She was a single mom in the '80s. She worked hard for the money (thank you, Donna Summer) and lived paycheck to paycheck. Her father would often give her money when she couldn't make ends meet. Money was always short and became one of the main topics my parents complained about to me, debating why my father was always late to send his child support checks and why she never seemed to have any for us—more adultification from them both.

Around second grade, my parents got into the habit of indulging me with their feelings and opinions about each other, sharing constant evidence of why the other parent was manipulative, hurtful, straight-up evil, and crazy. These rants started to provide me with fuel for understanding that both of them were similarly unhinged. If both were saying the other was bad, I concluded both of them were. My trust issues began there.

"Crazy" and "hyper-sensitive" were the main words used when I was screaming and pleading to be heard. My passionate hurt, frustration, and anger were fierce. Feeling enormously misunderstood and consistently being made to feel wrong for having feelings and opinions of my own, I eventually stopped sharing my views because it was too much energy to keep trying to be validated and understood. By the fourth grade, I started to distance myself from my parents and become independent, like a mini-adult. Their invalidation was consistently reinforced by their unconscious gaslighting, trying to convince me it was wrong to feel the way I felt. On the occasions I had to be with them, I could never contain the flood of hurt emotions that spilled out uncontrollably—much to my demise.

I had every reason not to trust my parents with my feelings and opinions. I doubt I'd have survived adolescence if it weren't for the honest conversations with my brother and aunt growing up.

I do not condemn them for their actions. Neither of my parents was aware of the effects of their words and actions. They were playing out their program. I'm not excusing them or blaming them. My story is my perspective. It is mine and only mine to tell.

The choice coping mechanism for escape

The elementary school I went to allowed us to walk to the stores down the block to buy lunch and candy. Not unheard of before the missing persons "milk carton" movement started right around that time. My first cigarette was among school peers during an off-site lunch break down the block from the school in the sixth grade. I didn't inhale. No one did. Shortly after that, I started smoking in the bathroom of my one-bedroom apartment, stealing one of my mother's Marlboro reds. Seeing myself as mature, sexy, and cool, I'd stand on the toilet to see my entire upper body in the mirror. When I first inhaled, I coughed so much that I thought it would never end. It was an initiation; the pain of the maladaptive coping mechanism was to cover up the sources of my emotional and mental torment. I became a pack-a-day smoker, toting a cup of joe on my way to seventh grade from the Q30 bus wearing my grandfather's checkered black and red hunting jacket. I looked hardened. I remember rolling the head of the glowing cigarette habitually on the left cuff, keeping it all neat and tidy. All grown up at 12, that was me. I pretended I had it all together while living in utter confusion from the chaos of my family dynamics.

Aside from the whole acting-out thing, I was a happy, go-lucky kind of kid. More like a hyper-active chicken without a head, impulsive, impatient, and needy. I was a bit of a Tomboy, a bit of a follower, and a typical misfit looking to belong yet always feeling somewhat out of sorts. I was chatty and starved for attention. My father's remarriage when I was ten only added more chaos to my life. It was insult to injury to the tenth degree. I was primed for the psychological abuse that was to come from her. It was a perfect storm that would first be my undoing and then later fuel my freedom.

Huan was my closest friend, and her home was my go-to for most of my elementary school years. I was the proud third wheel when she became good friends with Donna. We were Hewy, Dewy, and Louie, the trendy Disney characters characterized as the trouble-making triplets and Donald Duck's nephews. My one-bedroom basement apartment was a boring cage. I loved to go to both of their homes, where people engaged with me. I loved the extended family dynamics of Huan's three-family apartment home. Her uncles and aunts lived upstairs, and her grandparents lived on the top floor. They spoke Burmese and watched all their programs in Chinese. Though I didn't speak the language, the language of words was irrelevant. I never felt more accepted and comfortable just for being human. To this day, their traditional meals taste better than any restaurant ever. Although my dad taught me how to use chopsticks when we went out for family-style Chinese food, I perfected the art of using them at the Chan family residence. Beyond my skill with wooden sticks, I learned acceptance at their place and saw the contrast to my own home. My experience with that family taught me more about empathy and relationships than any other group of people. They accepted me because I existed. Love doesn't get any purer than that.

After my mom's music career didn't pan out in the early eighties, she spent her days working nine to five, then lying in bed writing in her diary. I don't remember many dinners together, but I recall many dinners in front of the television, which stayed on until the end of Johnny Carson's Late Show at midnight. We lived together, but it felt more like we were roommates than mother-daughter. When she stopped writing songs and playing her piano in hopes of making it in the music business, her main goal was to find a man to marry. She worked hard as a secretary, then as an insurance agent, but never could manage to get her head above water financially. From her vantage point, a husband was the only way to financial security. And only a mate could mend her chronic loneliness. I resented that she needed a man to consider herself a success in life. I wanted her to be stronger than she was. Not knowing it then, I was racking up resentment of her to last for a couple more decades. She was tuned out and uninvolved enough so I could do some damage to myself. My brother's teenage foibles with drugs and petty thievery inspired me not to go too far into the rabbit hole of derelict self-destruction. Instead, I used all the *socially acceptable* forms of additions to escape and numb out my emotional turmoil. I ate tons of garbage foods, binged on copious amounts of television, shoplifted when I knew I'd never get caught, and smoked cigarettes like a truck driver—all before my 13th birthday.

Mixed up, dazed, and confused

My father and mother's unresolved and hurt feelings overshadowed my entire experience growing up. Their dramatic stories were told and retold—repeatedly for as long as I can remember. My mom always accused me of being "off" and "not myself" when I came back from staying at my father's for the weekend. She told me he was brainwashing me, not that it wasn't true. My father loved to trash talk my mother, and I rather enjoyed it myself, having so much resentment for her shortcomings and disinterest in me. That was how my father and I bonded. I felt a certain kind of loyalty to him as my once-a-week Dad. I just wanted his acceptance and love. I was angry, frustrated, and overwhelmingly confused by all the drama coming from both sides. I could bitch 'til kingdom come about my mom when I was with him. He rather enjoyed taking inventory of my headspace. However, to no surprise, expressing any frustration or angst about him or his wife was totally off-limits. It was selective sharing; I was permitted to express myself so long as it didn't hit home too hard. And there we lived. I was loved as long as I didn't make any waves. His wife could go off on screaming sprees, but I wasn't allowed to complain about it. It infuriated me she had the freedom to express herself, and I didn't. She could hurl insults at me, and I was humiliated whenever I complained. He shut down whenever I spoke up about our dynamics. I kept trying to speak up, and time and time again was invalidated and minimized. Eventually evolving into feverish meltdowns, met with his angry resentment, frustration, and denial. He simply could not recognize the mistreatment his wife was inflicting on me. He turned a blind eye every time and then discredited me for every feeling or expression I had about the abuse I was experiencing from her. A rock in a hard place, indeed.

When I complained to my mother about my dad and how mean his wife was to me, her answer was to not go there if I wasn't comfortable. This only pissed me off more because I DID want to be with my father. What child doesn't want to be with their father? It took me years to realize I wanted her to swoop in and have a grown-up talk with my dad and his wife. I wanted her to protect me by setting a limit, standing up to my step-monster, and telling her to stand down. There was this back and forth where I played both sides, and both sides disappointed me tremendously. All is fair in love and war, and no one is innocent was what I learned from all of it. It got me nowhere but circling the drain all up in my parent's business as if there were nothing better to talk about. Boundaries simply didn't exist when relating with my parents. I didn't even know what they were until I began learning about narcissistic abuse in my mid-forties, three decades after living it.

However inadvertent, the emotional manipulation I endured bears a striking resemblance to the phenomenon of gaslighting. Gaslighting is loosely defined as making someone question their own reality. Also used to describe a person (a "gaslighter") who presents a false narrative to another group or person, which leads them to doubt their perceptions and become misled, disoriented, or distressed (generally for the gaslighter's own benefit). This dynamic is only possible when a group or person is vulnerable, having unequal power relationships, or when they are fearful of the consequences of challenging that false narrative. Gaslighting is not necessarily malicious or intentional, although in some cases it is.

Both parents' oblivious but effective gaslighting burned down any possible foundation of significant rapport. There was no real connection because there was no emotional safety. In time and after a lot of therapy, I learned to accept their limitations and accept the dimensions and scope of conversations as enough. There was no mal-intent, only denial, and ignorance. The void that existed by their lack of awareness, I sought to fill in with substitutes everywhere I wandered for decades to come.

Caught in the crossfire

In my adolescence, there was a pattern unfolding. When I was with my father, he'd always complain about how my mother was taking the child support money and spending it on herself. He thought the money should be spent on clothes, beyond the food on the table. I didn't know anything about it, but I listened to him and he listened to me ruminate about how unhappy I felt living with her. The child support dispute came to a head when I turned 18. My mom sued my dad for child support which he stopped paying the day I was a legal adult. He counter-sued, using my anger toward my mom against me. I, terrified and conflicted, testified as to why she didn't deserve the child support he was giving her. I didn't know the fine print of that legal contract at the time, and my mother didn't speak a word of it to me. My dad won the case, ending the child support agreement and releasing him from the legal obligation to pay for my college education. During this debacle, he told me I could not "straddle the fence" and had to pick a side. At the time, I picked his side because he would help me get on my feet as I went through community college. Emotionally though, I knew I could never side with him. Of course, my mother was devastated by my betrayal. I was a big ball of fear, confusion, and anger. After I transferred to Binghamton University, he stopped paying for my tuition. In a game of manipulation and revenge, I was a pawn annihilated and floating in the muck of their heartaches. My relationship with each of them was the casualty of their war.

This experience birthed a unique awareness I call polarity-consciousness; Extremes of either "side" are more similar than different. Both sides might be right if both sides were convinced the other side was wrong. Perspective is everything, after all.

Needless to say, the idea of marriage was revolting to me for many years to come. My grandparents on both sides had failed marriages. My parent's marriage was a trainwreck, and their new marriages didn't seem too wonderful either. Divorce ran in my family; I wasn't at all interested in it after all that drama. Of course,

I couldn't help myself from giving it a whirl twenty years later, failing miserably—just as my parents did. Failing forward, such is life. We are all doing the best with what we've got and rightfully own our point of view.

On with the programming

Every good story needs a villain for impact. The evil stepmother entered the scene when I was nine years old. She had an effortless disdain for my every breath, move, and word. I perpetually ass-kissed to gain her approval from that time until my late thirties, as if under some kind of trance. She had zero interest or respect for me. I enjoyed fleeting moments of kindness on very rare occasions, only to be followed up by some tragic incident that caused explosive anger and disappointment of some unforgivable mistake I inevitably made. She always was allowed to scream and bellow. I was not allowed to show my terror, nor was I permitted to feel my fear. She was superior to me, and everyone in the room agreed, including me. Of course, while I deeply resented being the token pee-on, I saw no other out that to submit to her dominance. The intermittent reinforcement of her acceptance was my main objective when I was in her home. I was addicted to her approval like a junkie is to heroin. Of course, usually, I was kept in craving, feeling unworthy of her favor.

This is what emotional abuse looks like. Deep down, I sensed her insecurity and jealousy, and she was merely projecting her discomfort onto me. I was public enemy numero uno as my father's daughter. She won. I only knew to yield, and it was a losing battle. She seemed to allude I was unworthy of my father's attention, which was the status quo. Until I learned the language of emotional intelligence and the psychology of healthy relating, I was held captive by feeling unworthy of love and affection.

Now I understand why everything happened exactly as it did. All the chaos brought the desire for simplicity. My emotional pain brought the desire for relief. The willingness to evaluate the past shed valuable perspective on these less-than-ideal dynamics giving birth to massive wisdom. The natural outcome of self-evaluation is emPOWERment. Our lives are opportunities to transmute the negative experiences into lessons of accountability and acceptance, then followed by forgiveness.

Personal alchemy looks like this

We're meant to learn from and then share stories to relate with others and inspire one another. Our story contains energy; that energy is latent until we can learn from what was given versus what was preferred. The contrast between the two lies the turbo-charge for attaining what we need from our life. What we experienced and didn't like makes us privy to what is desired. This contrast illuminates what matters to us; our priorities and values. Once you hit a threshold of discomfort in your life, the story stops being shameful and becomes a fuel source for transformation.

Our parents are teachers in disguise. Most parents did the damn best they could with all they were aware of at the time. Usually, wishing they knew better, looking back in hindsight. (Hindsight is 20/20, after all.) They didn't know that they didn't know. They didn't know they were bypassing, invalidating, abusing, or devaluing us. We didn't understand we were being bypassed, invalidated, abused, or devalued at the time. None of us had the language to identify the long-term impacts, and we were too busy living them. Most parents felt powerless to change their circumstances in the thick of the burden of raising children, as life seemed to spiral beyond their control. Or worse, their need for control made them blind to a greater perspective. Everyone did the best they could with all they possessed. As Maya Angelou reminds us, "When we know better, we do better." The following practice helps us put that intention into action.

The Ho'oponopono practice

A Hawaiian phrase that teaches reconciliation and forgiveness, Ho'oponopono is intended to correct an incorrect relationship. It is meant to heal the heart through visualizing other people and aspects of ourselves, setting ourselves free from resentments bringing peace into our hearts and serenity to the mind. This prayer can be practiced in many ways. Like breathwork, its application is diverse, and each one is equally as potent so long as there is a heartfelt involvement in its exercise. I like to envision that the person or aspect of myself that wants forgiveness is hearing it from the person or aspect of myself that says it. Something about visualizing and affirming these simple statements rewires the memory of the subconscious because anything the mind can conceptualize; it can believe as truth. This practice is a way to receive the apology you'll never receive from others and energetically apologize in cases where you're unable to apologize directly. Apologizing from our hearts to ourselves, the part of us that didn't know better when we acted in ways where we unintentionally or otherwise hurt ourselves and others, can be a powerful shift to deliver forgiveness to ourselves. The mere recognition of our mistakes brings clarity and raises awareness, changing our behavior eventually. Old habits do die hard, but this practice helps us mend the error of our ways.

The following four sentences, in any order, complete the Ho'oponopono prayer:

I love you.

I'm sorry.

Please forgive me.

Thank you.

See the Resources page in the back of the book for a Ho'oponopono meditation on YouTube.

Leveling the playing field

Very few of us, if any at all, had perfect parents, and most were deprived of the idealized parenting we envisioned. Frequently, the apparent needs and those needs we didn't even know we had were unmet. We took what we were given and didn't know what we were missing. We sensed something amiss as we were clueless about what we were missing out on. Faced with a ton of backlogged grief, many like me recall lacking and longing for what was not received. I wanted acceptance and emotional safety. I received contempt and rejection. The result often creates and repeats perpetual resentment cycles where no one wins. An egoic insatiability compounds this with loud cries of self-pity and self-gratification to shield oneself from further pain. While the intuitive voice, a gentle whisper, can only be heard when the ego is calm and feeling a sense of safety. These two voices are akin to the angel (higher consciousness) on one shoulder and the devil (ego) on the other. The angel wants peace and acceptance while offering unifying compassion. The devil dwells in chaos, problems, and dividing apathy. Or if they were the two wolves, as the old Cherokee fable states, the one that is fed the most will be the one that wins.

Unhealed wounds are loud

As a process of avoiding and defending ourselves from our painful emotional wounds during our childhoods, we projected our losses as resentments for their shortcomings in all the ways we hungered for. We ask ourselves in our frustrated anger and grief, "How dare they not do as we would have liked?" "How can they be so oblivious to our perspective?" "Where is their empathy?" "Why aren't they caring as I would if I were in their shoes?" The mind scrambles to make sense of how things were, wishing it were another idealized way. "If only" became our swansong, continuing the trend in our romantic endeavors with the same patterns of dissatisfaction and hurt.

Subconscious neediness is generational. As our parents were raising us, we couldn't acknowledge how impossible it was for them to meet our needs while their own needs and preferences were not met in their childhoods or ever healed in adulthood. We're frequently reminded that "You can't pour from an empty cup." While we intimately understand that it's only from our fullness that we can give to others, few had proper role models to demonstrate fullness and fulfillment. Instead, what was provided by parents who never had their own needs met was compensatory and often manipulative to have THEIR own needs met BY and through their children. As common as this is, it is another whole can of adult-child/parentification worms.

Deprivation creates desire

It is safe to say that most of us, at least most who care enough to read this far, were given too much of the things we didn't need and not enough of what we craved. *To add insult to injury, we were forbidden to complain about it.* The hunger for love began in this uncomfortable void; then followed the wacky attempts (i.e., maladapted coping mechanisms, addictions, and distractions) to feel some semblance of needs getting satisfied. Desire became our drug, soothing the emotional pain with sweets, snacks, cigarettes, beer, social drama, excessive entertainment, or shopping, to name a few of my quick fixes. Not knowing how to meet our needs, we reach for chosen substitutes and numbing substances or situations. Then, they become our routine method to deal with the void of the unmet need. These escape methods became automatic; unless and until there is a necessity to disrupt them.

Having no "blueprint" to learn how to meet our needs means there is no visible source to model from unless we learn to seek sources outside of what we're accustomed to. First, we must identify a missing need before we can fathom satisfying it. The initial inadequacy kept us from identifying what our actual needs were. Then, perpetual patterns of inadequacy ensue, all with that unsettling sense that something is profoundly missing in life. Unbeknownst to us, it's needs we never knew we had. Until we start to scratch beneath the surface with questions many are too fearful to ask.

Healing begins when we ask big questions like, "What was missing?" "What was given and not wanted?" and "What was wanted and not given?" The next step is to find a way to provide for what was lost and restore what was damaged—asking these questions and listening to your gut with honesty and compassionate humility. It is therapeutic to acknowledge the need, validate it, and give yourself the sensation of meeting your needs on your own or with the aid of others.

In my case, I longed for mothering. I always ached for my mother's love and focused selfless attention. I became the mother I always wanted to be; to myself. When I felt unseen, unheard, and misunderstood, I took notice instead of reactively taking some action only made it worse. By validating my need to be acknowledged, that hurt little girl inside immediately calmed, feeling seen, heard, and understood. It took my inner child a long time to trust me. I learned to have everlasting patience with her. For so long, my inner child was speaking through my emotions, but I ignored her, thinking I had better things to do. My diversions and distractions were so deeply ingrained that I didn't want to be bothered with validating my own feelings! That little kid waited for me to pay attention for a long time. She was relentless and stubborn, knowing I needed her to thrive. Her persistence was worth the wait; I am here for her as she always needed me to be. I was starved for my mother's love until I figured out how to nourish my inner child.

Hunger for mother

Growing up Jewish, my first religious concern was why God was a "He" and how there was no mention of women other than being men's wives? Perhaps this question burned inside me, as my father was not very present in my day-to-day life. My mother haphazardly ruled the roost. I saw her as weak and wished she had more energy and strength. I accidentally stumbled upon a book at the library that explained ancient cultures whose people worshipped the child-bearing, fierce mothering, and innate nurturing gifts of women, along with the sacred symbolism of menstrual blood representing fertility, abundance, and vitality. I was fascinated with the lack of shame that these matriarchal-centered cultures had. The timing was impeccable, right before my first period at age thirteen. I saw all the pictures of Goddesses as beautiful, voluptuous, and confident. There was no shame in their femininity. They glowed with the radiance of their character. It gave me hope as a female.

Meanwhile, from what I observed all around me, women's menstrual blood was revolting. It perplexed me that something so natural, which all women do, was viewed as repulsive. I remember being so confused by the cultural shaming of this cyclic bleeding, knowing that healthy fertile women had it and how it was the reason all of us humans came to be. I clearly remember the embarrassment of so many of my friends in anticipation of their coming fertile years. Yet, I could not wait for the sacred experience of getting my period.

It didn't make any sense. Many things didn't make sense to me when I was thirteen. Chaos and confusion being the norm, my being well acclimated to it. Still, I couldn't help but be outraged by this contradiction about menstruation. I refused to be ashamed of my body's natural and healthy function. I didn't mind the blood one bit when it finally arrived. I refused to be embarrassed to buy a box of sanitary napkins at the local grocery store. Buying them was no big deal, and I couldn't figure out all the unease and judgment around an innate female phenomenon. Little did I know the hypercriticism of everything feminine was just beginning.

It seemed to me that while men got to explore their world with curiosity, women were judged by a standard of perfectionism. I was a bit envious and resentful of men who seemed to be glorified while women were subservient to them from what I observed around me in real life.

I found camaraderie in the Neo-Pagan, New-Age Goddesses. Kali, an ancient Goddess in India, was prized for her transformative fury; Durga, also from India, is a deity of protection, and Kuan Yin, from China, the Goddess of Compassion. They became my role models, whereas the women around me seemed weak, self-absorbed, and cold. All of the women in my upbringing had strained relationships with their mothers. There was so much hurt, fear, resentment, and criticism. The multitude of Goddess, these intangible, mythical women from all over the world, were my heroes, as my real-life role models seemed miserable in their lives, lacking any semblance of gratitude. Due to my conditioning, as hard as I tried to avert it, I repeated that very pattern unknowingly until decades later.

I became thirsty for more knowledge of divine mother figures. There was comfort in exploring other religions in college and throughout my thirties. Eventually, Buddhism and Taoism drew me in. I dabbled in meditation practices but wouldn't sustain a regular practice until my forties. My deep resentments and lack of inspiration from the real world led me to a deeper discovery of philosophy and spirituality. I rejected patriarchal religions for most of my life until 2012, when I became puzzled with Jesus, driven by my daughter's birth, eventually leading me to my baptism in a lake in 2016. I felt a strange full-circle completion when I explored Jesus' life and symbolism. It released a big block, breaking down my barrier against the belief in a masculine God, having a breakthrough around my longing to be fathered in a meaningful way. Unknowingly, I had become very manly, gradually into my early forties. My self-awareness brought me more humility and honesty, so the layers of self-protection began to disintegrate. The unraveling of my preconceived hardened pretenses had been initiated, and divine suffering began to teach me the power of weakness I denied myself until then. In 2014, a gratitude and awareness practice slowly helped me reintegrate parts of my frailties and become my true self—peeling back all the layers to find the real me hidden deep within my cultural conditioning.

With dis-integration comes the promise of integration

Harmonizing my Yin (Feminine) and Yang (Masculine) energies, I needed to look beyond my biological parents to feel a meaningful connection with Spirit; the great Heavenly Father and great Earthly Mother; helped me to see aspects of myself with clarity. Realizing I am the offspring of these two greats divine forces, it took all the pressure off my insistence that my parents ought to nurture me as I always hoped for. I am a child of their communion; out of pure creation, I am made. With that orientation, a huge load was taken from my mind initiating the healing of my heart.

Making peace with my own Yin and Yang traits restored my sanity in many ways. Excessive one-sidedness is a blatant imbalance in the human body, according to Ayurvedic and Traditional Chinese Medicine (TCM). Both feminine and masculine energies exist as polarities, both necessary for balance. Together they bring wholeness (Oneness).

Why is balance important anyway? All health and well-being are built upon it. Too much Yang or Yin energy in a person predisposes them to illness of mind, body, and emotion, as TCM so eloquently presents as a general rule. Extremism leads to bias and skewing.

According to the U.S. National Library of Medicine and the National Center for Biotechnology Information, the polarity principle is defined as follows:

> The principle of "yin and yang" is one of the core theories of Chinese philosophy as well as of TCM (Traditional Chinese Medicine). Ancient Chinese philosophy holds that everything in the universe has two sides—yin and yang— which describe the properties of both the opposites and unity of interrelated things or phenomena in nature. According to TCM theory, one's physical health depends on harmony in the functions of various bodily organs, a moderate and stable state of emotional expression, as well as adaption to different environments, of which the most vital is the dynamic balance between yin and yang. TCM deems that illnesses are fundamentally due to the disturbance of the dynamic balance between yin and yang caused by external or internal factors. When yin and yang

are in a state of balance, the body is healthy. When the balance is disturbed, the body becomes unhealthy.[7]

Our physical bodies are constantly in pursuit of balance. The heart perfectly represents this polarity, circulating freshly oxygenated blood while pumping used blood out. Like the heart with two functions in one, yin and yang are two sides of a whole human.

The function of a defense mechanism is to bring balance where there can be none. It's entirely compensatory and wreaks havoc on the person in the habit of relying on it to function instead of achieving natural balance, impeded by obstacles and a lack of awareness.

Bred for submission

Both my maternal and paternal grandmothers were mediocre women with meager incomes, unmarried, and viewed as failures by their children. High-status women they were not. I remember little of them but the smell of cigarettes and the feel of vinyl on their couches. There's a certain brand of tragedy bestowed upon single women. This tragedy was passed down to me by my mother, who, finding herself divorced and on the perpetual hunt for a husband for most of my life, her MO was to not fall into this category of pitiful undesirables. Her desperation intrigued me. When I decided to travel across the country after college, my mom questioned my wanderlust, telling me how she wanted her M-R-S., at my age, not her P-H-D. Despite her prodding that I find a mate, it had the opposite effect. I needed to follow my curiosity and be

---

[7] https://www.ncbi.nlm.nih.gov/pmc/articles/PMC6880673/

free of such cultural constraints. Leaping into the unknown was the only place that made sense to me in my mid-twenties.

Amidst all the confusion and self-minimization conditioned in me by what I deemed my toxic and mutated nuclear family, fleeing the scene was the only safe option. Before I moved away to college, I continually vacated the scene and mentally disconnected to cope with being stuck in my family circumstances. My choice defense mechanism was dissociation. In this state, I could go into the safe place of my intellect, as I abandoned my own feelings to tolerate the blatant invalidation of my opinions and emotions so burdensome and annoying to my primary caregivers for the first twenty years of my life. Staying physically and emotionally present was inconceivable and not an option for me. As my adulthood progressed, I couldn't bear conversing with my mother, who always circled the topic back to herself, and it tortured me to listen to my stepmother's intricate jokes and self-indulgent stories about her escapades at the local grocery store while I was considered unworthy to speak.

In an article for PACES Connection, author Rebecca Mandeville MFT notes, "A healthy adult relationship requires that the two people involved create a relational environment that is reciprocal, truthful, respectful, and interdependent. If you are a "fawner," you may have not been sure if you were loved and accepted as a child, so you learned to meet the needs of others and appease them to prove your value and worth."[8] A categorization of stress responses discovered by Pete Walker MA at the turn of the millennium,

---

[8] https://www.pacesconnection.com/blog/the-trauma-response-of-fawning-aka-people-pleasing-part-one

fawning, is a more recently discovered stress reaction, adding to the "fight or flight and freeze" list. My flight was initially internal. I froze from fear on the regular, but then I started to "feed" as another way to cope with feeling unloved and not accepted. My people-pleasing (the most common fawn response to try and win the approval of others) was most obvious with my stepmother as I voraciously ate all her food offerings. It was my chosen path of least resistance, the pleasure, and the escape of filling my mouth to alleviate the pain of not feeling free to express myself. I bent over backward to gain recognition and approval until one day, I ran out of energy and instead went full-on into flight mode instead.

Inferiority, money, and drawing a line

Panic attacks weren't a thing in the '80s, or at least they weren't on my radar, but I suffered from a multitude of them EVERY time I visited my father from 1984 until I stopped going there around 2014. Something about his wife's stink-eye and relentless condemnation would set off my nervous system every time I was around her. Properly groomed for invalidating my feelings and opinions, I had a knack for minimizing myself, so someone with a superiority complex would be a great topper to compliment my life lessons and induce a regular state of intimidation. I was beyond horrified by my father's wife. She had all the power and seemed to get a kick out of abusing it. Panic-stricken and in a constant state of appeasement, my inferiority was programmed on a deep subconscious level. She seemed more intelligent, pious, sophisticated, and far more loveable—at least to my father—than I could ever hope to be. She commanded the room boldly while I was the designated wall-flower. Constantly criticized for everything but breathing, she groomed my father to see me as inept, mangy, and cunning. She depicted me to my father as an ill-mannered, defiant child who might steal someone's wallet if you didn't watch me. One smear campaign failed, as she told my father I was rummaging through his file cabinet to get him to believe I was trying to carry out some spy-tactic or who-knows-what on a rare incidence that I slept over their house. They had money and tokens of extravagance and class. I had none of those things, but I suppressed the outrage and jealousy of wanting any part of it. Needless to say, the rejection went pretty deep. It took my father twenty years of marriage to realize that his wife had deep mental and emotional troubles. I felt validated when he recognized there was a problem in her rage and intolerance of me. When I was nearing thirty, he sympathized with my perspective for the first time in my life. Too many never get this kind of recognition and acknowledgment from a parent. I'll always be thankful for a moment of honesty and mental wellness for us both.

Resenting money was a signature pattern in my life experience as a direct result of receiving the message that I was unworthy of the same gifts and financial support my father's second batch of kids, my half-brothers, enjoyed. Since I was not worthy of the same financial aid stature and attention, I defensively came to believe my self-worth was not reflected in the monetary value of my clothes. Ripping off the labels of my Keds sneakers and laughing at the twenty-dollar socks my friends prized, I rejected materialism almost completely, yet I repressed my desire for trendy things in my teens. Repressing my desires became habitual. I would deny my angst about luxury and status symbols while secretly being envious of the exact things I shunned. Because I was denied access and felt unworthy, I rejected my own desires. Witnessing the parade of Chanukah and birthday gifts showered on my half-brothers was emotionally agonizing. I felt lucky to get in a picture on birthdays and holidays. It appeared that every effort was made for them to feel loved in all the details a good party provides, while I, the modern Cinderella, was forced to swallow my pride and get left behind. There were no parties for little Cinder-Lisa. She was unworthy of such indulgences from the evil Queen who ruled over her domain and dolled them out to her biological children.

The occasional family gatherings I did attend diminished as I grew into young adulthood. Finally, the pretending could not continue any longer. It wasn't until my stepmother's mother died in 2018 that I drew a boundary *for the first time in my life*, alerting her that I would not listen to her talking anymore. Of course, I did so via email because it was far safer to do it behind a screen than face to face. I could not stomach sitting and subjecting myself to the dead-end conversations any longer. The one-way shallow grew too painful to endure.

At that moment, finally, my days of fawning and placation would cease. Taking full responsibility for my part in the damage would become my freedom ticket to a life I was proud of.

What it means to take power back

We are all products of our circumstances at the start. People who are marginalized within and outside of their family of origin are at a considerable disadvantage to flourish in health and prosperity. To overcome the programming of being forced into subordination requires an unlearning process, a re-programming of sorts, recognizing the projected value imbalance from one person to another. Generally, as a rule, the subordinate person is the one to realize a problem with the situation. When the subordinate person is motivated to step outside the dysfunctional dynamics and evaluate their beliefs, their realities shift for the better.

Walking away is easy. The real challenge lies in changing the habitual belief of a submissive orientation. Unlearning and re-programming beliefs, actions, and subconscious patterns are where the work is. The ineffective and marginalized practices keep showing up in different circumstances and people without consistent application and work to change them. Hence, the saying "wherever you go, there you are."

Then what?

In the first 25 years of life, we are not fully developed in our minds. Neurologists agree that the prefrontal cortex of our brain becomes fully developed at age 25. This fact is important because "The prefrontal cortex (PFC) plays a central role in cognitive control functions, and dopamine in the PFC modulates cognitive control, thereby influencing attention, impulse inhibition, prospective memory, and cognitive flexibility,"[9] according to Science Direct.

Before age 25, humans are sponges caught in a whirlwind of confusion and mixed messages. After that, the responsibility lies on you to straighten out all the messes in your head. We venture into young adulthood doing our darndest to make ends meet and create a life that doesn't suck. The concept of independence is like

---

[9] https://www.sciencedirect.com/topics/medicine-and-dentistry/prefrontal-cortex

a golden horizon calling. Mesmerized, we follow it under the spell of the promise that life will be better than childhood and adolescence. Our patterns only follow us until we have the gumption to face the unresolved stuff. That's where the freedom is, cleaning up the mess so we can live without the debris of our past cluttering our present and future.

Stillness in Action

Make this a ten or twenty-minute exercise. Consider the following while completing the Ho'oponopono prayer for yourself:

✓ Visualize the phrases, "I love you, I'm sorry, please forgive me, thank you." Imagine the scene as you desire and with whom. You can choose a group or an individual to practice with at first. First, doing the prayer only one way, either receiving the blessing for yourself or gifting it to another.

✓ Notice what surfaces in your heart and mind, and pay attention to the thoughts and feelings that come up during and afterward.

✓ Play with the practice by trying it in reciprocation. Both give it and receive it. Observe again what surfaces in your heart and mind during and afterward.

Action in Stillness

✓ Journal the visualization itself and how it played out. Explore the effects of practicing it after the first time or as many times as you so desire. Describe the reflections of your observations of the thoughts and feelings that come up and after the exercise.

Action Initiative

Do this exercise for seven days, upon waking or right before bedtime:

✓ Journal or reflect on how you relate to the dynamics of giving and receiving the Ho'oponopono prayer throughout the week.

✓ Notice if there were any shifts in your awareness of how you relate to receiving or gifting the blessing.

3

"Most safely shall you tread the middle path."

—Ovid 43 BC–– 17 AD

Chapter 3

Hyper-Independence

"When you shut down emotion, you're also affecting your immune system, your nervous system. So, the repression of emotions, which is a survival strategy, then becomes a source of physiological illness later on."
—Gabor Maté

Stumbling forward while pretending to have it together

There is a ton of pressure to have our shit together after high school, no matter our plans. If we don't have a plan, the consensus is that we are screwing ourselves and setting our lives up for failure. Driving a car and voting in elections seemed promising in practicing this idea called maturity, although I'm sure many can admit we did not feel like an adult at 18. Being all grown up is not something I felt any likeness of until my mid-thirties. The road to adulting was beyond meandering for me. Unquestionably, I took an incredibly scenic route to maturity. My free-spiritedness was always tamed by my sensibility, having no trust funds or silver spoons in my mouth. There was no room to dawdle. I had to earn my keep. Ambitious and driven, after bouncing back from truancy, I saved my own academic ass in the last year and a half of high school.

Forward, backward, high, and low

Thoroughly confused, frustrated, and annoyed in my childhood and adolescence, I sought to escape as often as possible. Graduating from high school was an epic drama, coupled with the lows of a near-failing GPA and the pot-induced highs on the outdoor bleachers of the football field. Smoking weed was a habit I picked up in the seventh grade, along with my comrades. By tenth grade, aside from being a pack-a-day smoker of cigarettes, the pot was an obsessive pastime and my main dissociative escape. I belonged to a group of kids who seemed to tolerate me, as I was practically crawling out of my skin with emotional turmoil and mental agitation. I didn't have any deep connections. We had in common our affinity for cutting class and doing whatever psychedelic drugs were available to alleviate our chronic discontent.

Over the years, as I habituated my use of cannabis, I noticed how I wanted to "just say no" when the bowl or bong was passed to me. The thrill of the high didn't feel good, and I didn't much like the stupor it put me in. Yet, as the pot came to me, it automatically went to my mouth. This instinctual action was my first awareness of how muscle memory (and addiction) works.

At the tail end of tenth grade, I crushed on a clean-cut preppie guy who resembled Jake Ryan's character from the John Hughes movie, *Sixteen Candles*. Like Jake, this crush had deep brown eyes and a cute butt. After a few failed attempts to get his attention, he remained a stranger to me, ever so skeptically socially distant. After hearing rumors that I liked him, he curiously investigated who I was and pragmatically opened to a romantic relationship with me. When I met him, I wanted to do better in school, quit smoking cigarettes, and cut back on the pot, so being with this clean-cut, smart guy helped me succeed in a miracle 180-degree turn-around that was easier than I thought. I merely changed from one fish tank of friends to another. My self-soothing priorities quickly shifted from smoking things to eating things. Plus, frequently having sex was a great solution to all the emotional pain I continually felt and didn't want to acknowledge. Thanks to the comfort of my very own Jake Ryan, my grades went from barely passing to a B+ in my junior year of high school.

It wasn't even hard. All I did was show up and give a damn. I went on to community college with a passion for academia I never had. It was evident to others too. My English 101 teacher asked me a question I'd never forget. He said, "You are very bright. Do you know you're bright?" My reply was blunt. I said, "No, people always told me I was weird, so that's what I thought I was." Bright was a new one for me.

At 18, this was the first time anyone clued me in to having any intelligence in my life. Who knew curiosity was a sign of intelligence? I always figured it was me being a pain in the ass by asking questions that seemed to irritate my parents and befuddle my friends. Community college was an actual breeze of doing the work, cramming for tests, and getting straight A's. I barely applied myself and aced all my classes.

I chose one school where I wanted to finish my bachelor's degree and one school only. Binghamton University was the best SUNY (State University of New York) school in the system, and I didn't want to settle for anything less. My aunt was curious, asking why I'd choose such a competitive school. She asked, "Do you want to be a small fish in a big pond or a little fish in a big pond?" I answered, "Small fish in a big pond, so I have room to grow."

My choice to go to Binghamton University symbolized a standard of excellence. I didn't want a false sense of triumph; being a big ego in a little circle, I wanted a real-world experience. I wasn't interested in the competition at all. There was more to life than being competitive. I wanted to flourish at a school that could make me feel proud. Education status from a "good" school was the validation I was really after. When I got my acceptance letter, it was my first taste of discriminating approval. Having chosen environmental studies as my major for my first semester, I had a sudden challenge. My father disapproved of this study area so strongly, that he cut me off monetarily (or that was his excuse). I figured out how to declare myself financially independent to get loans to finish school with the help of the financial aid office and a few tears of anguish.

At a party, he complained to his friend how disappointed he was I didn't study pre-law or pre-med. To him, there was absolutely no value in the "hippy-dippy field of environmental studies." Thankfully, his friend came to my defense, relaying to my father that environmentalism was necessary for the future and how my education would be essential and beneficial—to the world at large. I smirked with satisfaction.

Stuffing my face and swallowing my pride

I never voiced my hurt and frustration towards my father about his decision. It was his way of guiding my college decisions toward a more profitable focus, so I knew I didn't have a leg to stand on as far as getting him to understand my point of view. Silencing myself seemed the safest route, but brooding over situations of significance would haunt me in my resentments. It was a trend I was oblivious to. I had to suck it up and swallow my pride, building frustration to save face. Blind to my own behavior at family gatherings, I stuffed my face as I stuffed my feelings and opinions. My ideas and emotions appeared to be completely unacceptable and something I was repetitively shamed for. Being shut down continually, I learned to stifle myself so that I was riddled with frequent panic attacks and couldn't be more verbally constipated.

But the food was delish! It was how I managed my family visits, stuffing it in and stuffing it down. There, my unexpressed emotion festered, infecting my body slowly over time.

I must've heard the phrase "When will you just get over it?" a thousand times whenever I whimpered about being less than pleased with some familial injustice. I wouldn't get over it by being shamed into getting over it. In fact, the inquisition only made my resentments—and appetite—stronger.

Bulimia, anorexia, and binge eating are all recognized as disordered eating. Emotional and compulsive eating are the foundation upon which all disorders are built. Eating until beyond full, I ached to feel satiation while being emotionally starved for love and acceptance. Stuffing my belly silenced my mouth from speaking words I longed to express but were shunned in my family.

If I weren't afraid of being truthfully expressive in my family relationships, I'd have had no need to feel the need to satisfy myself with food. My fear of freely communicating became the rationale for not only overeating but also overdoing it with other indulgences like social media, shopping, drinking, and consuming cannabis to soothe my discomfort of feeling anxiety, grief, or any other uncomfortable emotion that happened to rise up in me. In the culture where I live, any desired food is a very easy thing to get. It's so easy to satisfy a specific food craving. Food can seem the ultimate pleasure provider when social dynamics feel anything but. Eating compulsively often goes under the radar of addiction because we eat for sustenance and celebration. One cannot eliminate food in the same way they can stop using other harmful substances like alcohol or drugs. The habitual eating behavior to alleviate anger, outrage, sadness, and frustration get us to "bite our tongue" makes it the ultimate enabler of stifling our true beliefs and opinions in most social situations.

I've progressed and had healthy growth around my food consumption and boundaries in relating. It's been a gradual and gentle process of awareness. As my hunger for validation and being valued wasn't recognized in the past, I flooded my body chemistry with dopamine induced from many addictive behaviors, the main one being overeating harmful substances like salty and sugary snacks, alcohol, and empty carbs only fueled the fire for feeling bad about myself. Old habits die hard, much like stopping a train rushing full throttle. Mindfulness is key to slowing the train down long enough to witness one's own defense mechanisms.

Stopping the bypassing habit

Completely denying the validity of our own opinions and feelings takes a lot of energy and cultivates a special kind of doubt and resentment when being subordinate becomes a way of life. To avoid conflict, we become subservient, constantly monitor others, and assess their contentedness. It's a full-time job to be that honed into others' feelings instead of our own. More than a job, it actually defines codependency. A hard pill to swallow, but it fits the bill. The external focus on others' feelings instead of our own creates unhealthy relationships with ourselves and those around us.

Keeping the "peace" requires an excessive investment of external awareness. The façade of peace is a coverup, requiring subconscious bypassing of the inner turmoil that accumulates with every act of submission and "turning the other cheek." This subjugation is the birthing place of codependency and hyper-vigilance (the elevated state of constantly assessing potential threats around you). Only an intervention of sorts can stop this pattern. The mere recognition is the start of disrupting the pattern. Awareness and validation of a new understanding are more powerful than we give ourselves credit for. A step beyond commiseration and complaining, witnessing our role with a desire to do something different creates the momentum to move forward and leave the submissive behavior behind.

It appears few people dare explore the feelings that exist behind the desire to eat emotionally. When I first created the IMI method, it was to help me heal my chronic low-energy. I ached for a fun, easy way to get exercise while feeling too tired to do anything rigorous. I hated the gym and felt silly watching videos and following them. It felt lonely and awkward. I designed something for people like me who felt blocked and simply wanted to do something effortlessly and have that be enough. Little did I know that what I was eating stole my energy and was slowly creating dis-ease in me. IMI helped me get moving, cultivating body awareness to enable me to care more for it.

The embodiment practice I created develops the habit of uncensored and honest *observation* of one's feelings, peaceably guiding you through the process. Using the experience as a tool for emotional observation and physical expression, you'll find it a relief to have a refreshed connection to your emotional state instead of always reacting to them subconsciously and oftentimes destructively. (I describe this method in chapter nine.) Our throats follow suit when we learn to uncensor ourselves in our bodies. Suddenly, we realize we have a voice and are no longer afraid to say what's our minds and express our hearts. This expansion is internal, changing how we relate to ourselves, and then radiates outward to how we relate to everybody else. My technique takes the pain out of the dreaded "the way out is through" concept of healing and facing the parts of ourselves that we carry judgment around. As Poet and non-fiction author Diane Ackerman states, "Play is the brain's favorite way to learn." Play is more potent as a teacher than seriousness, and my methodology practices that.

Revisiting the escape and avoiding the holding pattern

I couldn't bear the energy-taxing demand of my own submission, being constantly gaslit and invalidated so regularly. I was always jumping out of my skin around both sides of my family. Once I had the power of my sovereignty after high school, I stopped wanting to be around them, and I rarely picked up the phone to initiate contact. Busy with their own life dramas, we barely kept in touch. I'd grown tired of them asking me the same questions repeatedly, and I could sense them tuning out as I responded. I figured, "Why bother talking if they couldn't listen?" I was always angry and frustrated about it and chose to visit less and less.

I noticed a generational pattern operating in my family's background. It was a dynamic where the mothers and their offspring were let down by one another. My parents had massive resentments toward their mothers, who missed the mark and failed at motherhood. I imagine my great-grandmothers were disappointed in their daughters being divorced, like divorces discontented my mother (yes, plural). It seemed I was following a script I didn't know the role I was playing, passing the torch of the same grief and sadness while repressing how much it weighed me down.

Still, I missed them and ached to be with them. I spent decades with a continual torn feeling of longing for their company but knowing I couldn't be in a room with them for more than an hour without at least one or two glasses of wine, a handful of snacks, and at least one bout of anxiety. Mostly, I craved an ideal familial scenario where I felt safe and understood by everyone. I see how self-centered of me that unrealistic expectation was. Ownership has its privileges, as now I feel released from such oppressive expectations to be around my family of origin.

Everywhere you go, there you are

Wherever I was during college, after college, whatever state of the country, a part of me noticed the patterns, but my overwhelming and suppressed feelings of powerlessness persisted. I denied how inadequate I truly felt. Instead, I wore a mask of fierceness, feigning strength and believing I was in charge of my life. I kind of was, in a runaway train sort of way. Inwardly, I was wildly led by my emotions, with my impulses driven by morose fears and insecurities.

There are many paths to go in life, and the only compass is our morals, no one else's. With me as my own captain, life was leading me where it was destined to go—not that I knew it at the time. Instead, I followed the stars, only seeking relief from the waves of anxiety and depression that I wouldn't become aware of for almost two more decades.

Oblivious to my own turmoil, it stemmed from deep loneliness, which I clouded with my serial monogamy. The romantic relationships got me through, but I still felt closed off and unable to trust deeply. After being cheated on in college, I swore off relationships between ages 24 and 29 and wore the non-committal cloak for a few long, disheartening years. The pattern of "Tarzan swinging" from long-term relationship to long-term relationship had worn off its allure by then. The notion of settling down evoked disgust. Financial goals were boring to me. I still was passionate about organic farming, poetry, psychology, philosophy, and spirituality. I became almost a glutton for growth, perhaps even addicted to it. Clueless about who I was, I let my curiosity guide my life. At school, I majored in environmental policy and administration and loved renewable resources, sustainable economics, and organic agriculture concepts. My studies led me to wonder about how to fix the world and how to fix myself. I pursued healing myself and this earth from mismanagement and malalignment with a vengeance.

In college, I discovered the Beatniks. The Beat Generation was a literary movement started by a group of authors whose work explored and influenced American culture and politics in the post-war era of the 1950s. For the first time, I felt I belonged; I was a beatnik, a member of the group of misfits that lived to question authority and the status quo while living for freedom.

After reading *On the Road* by the iconoclastic Beat Poet and writer Jack Kerouac, I knew I was one of them. I started to write more poetry (I dabbled in high school, very privately). When writing, I was immersed in my honest feelings, isolation, and huge resentments with the world. I began tapping into the universe of self-help books, bringing comfort to my shut-down, broken heart. I read at open mics on campus, breathing through my low self-esteem-rooted panic attacks. Someone told me my poems were "too much." Of course, this wasn't the first time I'd heard my words land on others like this. It bothered me, but I was used to having my words rub people the wrong way. It only strengthened my resolve, "I yam what I yam, and that's all that I am." declared the existential philosopher, Popeye, the sailor man.

There was comfort in digging deeply into my pain. I sensed splinters embedded in my skin and knew that poking and prodding would eventually lead to relief. Even if the fragment was never found or removed, I learned later that acceptance of my past and my feelings would deliver me to my emPOWERment. But for now, I was in the midst of the drama of my perpetual chaos, and things got worse before they got better. I wanted to take the needle and poke around some more, wanting resolution and acceptance where there was none available.

Before my first marriage at thirty-four, I had two more boyfriends in two different states a few months apart. They provided more learning experiences and a bit more drama. I settled down with a nice Jewish boy from Long Island, and our budding romance was a perfect storm of identity confusion combined with a long-standing craving to feel wanted by my father and his side of the family. Our adventure began with a two-carat diamond on my finger and a house in Syosset less than a year after meeting him. We were engaged six months in and married three months later. What was the rush? I was too clueless to know.

Around and around, we go

A year after graduation, I bought a one-way plane ticket and learned how to grow organic, biodynamic, permaculture veggies in beautiful Mendocino, California, which kicked my dysfunctional ass. I smoked, I drank, I cleansed, I sweat-lodged. Had I known I was a mental mess, instead of merely believing I was a free spirit, I'd have labeled the experience a nervous breakdown with constant surges of anxiety, depression, and desperate loneliness. After Y2K safely came and went, my father asked me to move back to New

York because he missed me. I'd never heard him utter these words before. I felt wanted and needed by him, maybe for the first time ever. I quickly began to make arrangements to come home.

I had to find my own place to live, of course. The tensions were still high with my dad's wife because I was me (oil), and she was her (water). I decided to stay with my bizarre and somewhat scary uncle David. This arrangement was not a smart move, as his penchant for hating on women was pretty intense. He always blew me away with his meandering super-charged, perfectionistic, and abysmal mind. The living situation at my uncle's was less than desirable. His house, full of teenage children, his mail-order bride from Vietnam, her daughter, and me, was a trigger-fest. There was a constant pull between subordinate and oppressive narcissistic traumatization between him and me. Realizing I was pulled back into the vortex with nowhere psychologically safe to live, the pattern remained with my parents. I quickly exited upstate to Ithaca, New York, to stay with an old college acquaintance with a few hundred bucks and my well-used Ford Tempo to start out.

Music heals the soul

At 27, I high-tailed it to Ithaca, the home base of my favorite college band, Donna the Buffalo. That band was a solace throughout my lonely college years. Their spiritual lyrics soothed my aching heart, and the groupies became my community; that town was my latest utopian ideal.

Ithaca was definitely a grass is greener sort of place. After my journeys in Mendocino, California, in 1999, I only wanted to be a country girl because the slower pace calmed me—except my inner turmoil and "city-girl" anxiety always kept me from being still for too long. I had some passionately vegan and very cool friends. They accepted me, and I appreciated them, which helped my social life immensely. However, my ability to hold down a job was nil. My job as a youth program coordinator for a local non-profit that worked as a go-between for the town and Cornell University was excellent, but it ended only after a year after running low on grant funds. I worked at two health food stores for a few months here and there. Rent was super cheap in Ithaca, and for two years, I kept moving from apartment to apartment every three to six months. I got tired of it, so I decided to plan an escape and couch surfed 'til I found another town to move to. I got a case of scabies from a festival I went to and spread the joy to a few of my kind and compassionate friends who let me crash in their living rooms. It was weird times for me in I-town. A friend wanted to leave Ithaca and try Buffalo, so I jumped at the opportunity. There wasn't much green grass in Buffalo, but I was curious if THAT was where my utopian and ideal life existed! Setting out to get used to change, I was skilled at leaving and starting over—and over, again and again. It wasn't long before I realized I was in a new town, with a new life and the same damn issues, frustration, and loneliness.

Everywhere I go, there I am

Ithaca wins the prize for being my rock bottom, or maybe it was Buffalo. It doesn't really matter which city was the "winner," both were sublimely the darkest, most depressing times of my life. I was in a hole, and I knew it. I remember a strange desire to call out to myself but felt ashamed as I whispered, "Help." I had to make an effort to raise my voice to hear my own plea. "Help!" I said aloud to myself while journaling a few times. I was isolated and writhing in emotional agony from feeling so independent and disconnected from a family that didn't seem to know what to do with me and my endless soul-searching for connection. I went to therapy for some support. It helped to have someone to talk to—until I left for the next utopian ideal.

Hanging out with mostly vegans then, I started to notice my digestive issues. When I ate certain foods like soymilk, tofu, ice cream, legumes, and seitan (pure wheat gluten), I'd get gut-wrenching gas pain and massive bloating. I had a constant state of anxiety, even paranoia, and ADHD-like symptoms that felt like a cruel joke from God.

I gained sixty pounds "trying" to be vegan and failing miserably. As much as I ate vegan treats and meals five to six times a day but always felt infinitely unsatisfied and heavy. Then, I started to cut out the soy, the gluten, and the dairy, but I always had some if I really wanted it and suffered the consequences shortly thereafter. I didn't do deprivation, that cut way too deep for the pain I was carrying around with me from moment to moment. This would be the start of my awareness of having remorse for eating things I shouldn't. Two more decades of this to figure my way out of it.

I knew I was a disgrace in the eyes of my family, but I refused to admit it. I always felt like I was doing the wrong thing. Shame and guilt drove my train; it was my cross to bear. I carried that cross unconsciously for the first ten years of the millennium. I couldn't shake the shame that ruled me. I was so enmeshed with it that I didn't recognize it as an emotion. It was a way of being. I was the embodiment of shame while dancing with fear. I was so unsettled inside of myself. I rejected my family's values but still wanted their approval. I feared connection to others, romanticized vague acquaintances and strangers, and ran from my own shadow from town to town all over the country. Every new area seemed to have the hope of permitting me to find a home within myself.

If it only weren't for those hurricanes

I moved from Buffalo to Maine, then to Florida in search of "home." I reached out to my Grandma Bea, my mother's stepmother, and my grandfather's second wife, who lived in Lake Worth, Florida. Bea was a nurturing and headstrong lady, open-minded and progressive for her time, she took me to get my second earholes pierced in the sixth grade, and I thought she was the coolest Grandma ever. She was always loving and kind to me. She knew what love was; my aunt was raised by her and seemed to have a better grasp of what love was than my mother, and I attributed that to her. I wasn't her granddaughter by blood, but I felt loved like hers. She moved to Florida shortly after my grandfather died. I wanted to be close to her to try and heal that putrefying stepmother wound I was carrying around everywhere I roamed. By articulating that as my reason to move there, something in me was healing—as slowly and delicately as I could handle. It was nice in Florida—if it weren't for those crazy hurricanes. Of course, I left Florida after two years, shacking up with a traveling cable man who took me to Louisiana, where I found random work through a temp agency. It took a few months for me to come to my senses. I left him in Missouri and went back to California.

Instead of Mendocino, I ventured inland. I settled in Sacramento, where a Mendocino friend was now living, and stayed with her until I landed my next live-in boyfriend. I got a job at Verizon in the customer service call center. It was treacherous. I felt like an actual slave with timed bathroom breaks and penalties for taking too long at the toilet. Their corporate culture felt like a bizarre cult. At first, it felt like membership in the Verizon cult was excellent because of the high hourly rate and health benefits. However, it didn't take long to discover how oppressive my job was.

I needed to escape—again. Running away to start over got old, painfully old, six years into the next millennium. I was in Sacramento less than two years before realizing it was time to stop running away and face my demons back home.

My strategies for finding a utopia failed. Escape and avoidance didn't pan out, much to my chagrin. Everywhere I went, there I was. My own annoyances and burdens followed me where ever I roamed. Home was where all the answers were. As intimidating as they were, I was sure of it. There's no place like home (clicking my heels three times in ruby red slippers). I sensed I had to be brave and give in to the gravitational pull of home base. I believed this time would be different. In 2007, I surely was a mature adult, or so I thought.

Into the storm

Speaking to my dad, he told me I should move back. I loved hearing how he wanted me to be close. My inner child did a little dance in hopes we'd be able to heal the past wounds between his wife and me. I wanted the same dream he did. Now to find a place to live, for everyone knows, I should be close, but not too close.

My brother needed a nanny for their new baby. I needed a home near my family. Perfect. At first, it felt great to be home and in the family system from the perspective of living with my brother, his wife, and their new baby. At thirty-three, I was living for the day with no real plan other than taking care of their daughter five days a week. My brother's basement was the business office for my father and himself. My dad offered me an opportunity for a few months of nannying. It involved checking mathematical equations for the company while the baby was napping. It did not go smoothly. He was a strict trainer, and I felt completely inadequate as he tried to teach me the procedures. I never had an interest or skill in anything mathematical beyond geometry. I had a wobbly foundation, barely knowing basic multiplication. I've had math anxiety since I was in grade school. I wanted to please him and for him to be proud of me. Deluded, I made myself believe I'd learn the rules in a few months and be on the family team. He tried to entice me with ridiculously generous pay to oversee accounts. The painful truth no one wanted to face, I was simply unqualified for the job. He wanted me in the family business so badly. To him, it was the solution to all my problems. Explaining to him that this wasn't going to work broke his heart as much as his desire to manage my life. Letting him down brought a surge of guilt and shame, but of course, I was oblivious to my feelings; they went invalidated and minimized as they always were before. I began to look for a real job, as the nannying job needed to also come to an end.

There I was, again in my submissive patterns, only closer to home and more surreal. I pretended all was well while still feeling vaguely miserable and out of place all the time. Something was not right, and I assumed it was something I could figure out, something outside of myself. I got the geographical itch again, fantasizing about moving to Vermont to escape the Babylon I was living in. Instead of making another move, I took the path of least resistance, found a great job working for a solar company, got a cute little apartment not far from my brother's, and began looking for love via online dating. Skilled at bypassing my wants and needs, I was chugging away on autopilot.

I waffled between a desire to fit in and a violent knee-jerk reaction to escape. As hard as I tried, I didn't fit in, and I couldn't understand why. Still crawling out of my skin, I wanted more than materialistic security and status. I wanted meaning and depth. I wanted real connection and compassionate communication. I wanted my family to want those things too, and I couldn't understand why they didn't. They seemed to resent me for my values as much as I resented them for theirs.

The storm of perfection

In my feeling of chronic loneliness and growing boredom, I felt the pull of settling down and wanting a sense of normalcy in my life. I was sure that a sense of belonging would come if I had a normal life. I miserably dated for many months. I was always pining for guys who didn't want me and minimizing those who did (what attachment wounds?). Apparently, JDate, the premier Jewish dating website, was the place to find a nice Jewish man to settle for, I mean, settle down with. Continuing to minimize my pagan and multi-spiritual proclivities was just automatic by now. I met a "very nice" veterinarian from Syosset who found my uniqueness titillating. He was relieved to find someone different from the

71

usual Jewish American Princess type. Oh, he found different, alright.

At first, I had zero attraction, and I told him so. But because he was wild about me and persistent, I gave him a chance. He went all out to impress me on our first date. It was chilly, and I didn't have a proper coat on, so I had to hold onto his arm while we stood in line at the Blue Note Jazz Café, where I'd always wanted to go since I learned about Miles Davis back in college. It didn't take much. That arm holding cast a love spell on me. Then and there, I could imagine him as my mate. He stood for all the right things my family valued: practicality, financial security, social acceptability, and Judaism. This man became my ticket to gain acceptance from my family, so I thought. Everyone loved his level-headed, pleasant company; he was a perfect buffer for me at family gatherings. My brother's wife and my stepmother had gotten closer since I moved out of my brother's place. The catty dynamic between them was tangible, now having that energy of two against one. I wasn't like them, and that was bad; I felt unworthy of their appreciation. Never mind my rejection of their values, I saw myself as a victim. As oblivious as I was of my own victimization, my judgment of them was as harsh as their opinions of me. As usual, I overfilled myself with food and drink at family gatherings to soothe the unbearable pain of my own frustration and isolation. My nice new partner was a pawn in my world of hurt. He was also soon to be another casualty of my inner war.

Bleeding on the inside

The solar electric business was great, but my interest in selling solar panels waned with the intensity of the competition among the companies. I was conditioned to back down from competition by my stepmother. I hated the pressure, which subconsciously triggered my inferiority complex. I recoiled from the dog-eat-dog sales environment to stick with my safe desk-based admin work. I bolted, as I always did.

The occasional headaches I suffered from since I was a kid became unbearable and constant around then, having them three or four days a week—the massage school around the corner from where we lived kept calling out to me. The pain in my neck was the main impetus for going. I wanted to give the massages I craved. Too many times, my requests for an effective neck massage fell on deaf ears of massage therapists. It annoyed me that so many of them were so unskilled with such a crucial area of the body notorious for chronic tension and pain. I decided I was going to be a neck massaging master! Off to massage school I went in 2009. I became a full-time massage therapy student, leaning on my new husband to cover my living expenses while I maxed out on loans to pay my tuition.

The daydreaming about moving to Vermont continued in the throes of my new marriage. I was at a surreal apex of cognitive dissonance. As we moved into our (his) new home on a quarter-acre lot a block away from his father. Physically, I was present, but emotionally I was nowhere to be found. I felt torn, living my life in a subdivision in the middle of Syosset, Long Island. When I told him I dreamed of living in Vermont, he laughed at me, telling me how cute I was. I started to demonize him, yet I was only minimizing myself, and he merely reflected it. I began to accumulate reasons to bail out of the marriage. Our sex life was a bore. His fixation on politics annoyed me. The arguments he had with his father made me weary (as all heated conflict did). It haunted me of all the past dramatic theatrics I had been a part of growing up by witnessing their loud and verbally abusive fallouts. Instead of communicating my concerns with my new husband, I created my escape plan in secret. All I had to do was finish two more semesters of massage school, pass the boards, then be on my merry way, off to la-la land of starting over once more.

Wherever I go, there I am

My plans changed. Life had taken quite the turn by the happenstance of Facebook's "people who you may know" feature. I had tried to find the whereabouts of a particular old flame back in the days of Myspace a few years prior. Before then, while visiting home from college, I stopped by his house, shocked to find it completely vacant. He was nowhere to be found since we decided to end our puppy-love affair in 1990 when he was shipped over to serve in the army during the Gulf War. In 2010, 20 years later, there he was in the bottom right corner of my computer screen. My legally-married heart was a flutter. I quickly sent a message, and he replied immediately. We met for dinner and walked around a bit afterward. It was just like old times when we were teenagers. Only now, I was a recently married woman.

It became clear to me and reinforced by the thrill of finding a long-lost lover how the life I'd been living was all a lie. My life at the time pleased my family but left me unfulfilled and experiencing an agonizing soul death. I'd taken such bold liberties; I'd gotten accustomed to being obedient only to my soul, to a great degree, for most of my life. I certainly couldn't maintain any other allegiance for long. The welcomed turnaround that gained me access to a sensation nearly resembling family acceptance (marrying the quintessential Jewish husband) turned into a total U-turn, then a b-line to my wild-hearted authenticity. Talk about theatrics.

Sharing a kiss with my sweetheart from twenty years prior sealed the deal. After the second time we reunited, I began to concoct an escape plan. It was not well executed. I broke the nice Jewish boy's heart after shocking it with the news I was leaving him, as I was in the process of packing up, no discussion. In the middle of January, I moved into a camper in some acquaintance's backyard in Northport. That lasted a month before I moved in with my old but new man. It took two months for me to get knocked up by my fantasy blue-collar army veteran. I was thirty-seven years old. The massive letdown of my family was off the charts. The choice was made, the nice house on the Island was not for me, and it burned up in smoke as my pregnant belly grew. My parents and siblings didn't speak to me until just before my daughter was born. Back to making my own decisions again, this time, there was no turning back as the bridge went up in flames.

The scarlet letter "A" stands for audacity

While I was theoretically free from my family's hold over me, I hadn't wholly owned the price of that freedom. I still walked with the shackles of their judgment wrought with guilt. I cared more about being part of my family than I could admit. All of it was too overwhelming. I resented my needing them. My current circumstances felt National Enquirer worthy with the way my family responded to my erratic antics. I imagined the headline as follows: "Nice Jewish Girl (but clearly crazy) Leaves Nice Jewish Boy for Uneducated Blue-Collar Man and is Having His Baby." The internalized shame crushed me, and my anger towards their condemnation overshadowed my pregnancy. The air seemed thicker than concrete, and the conversation was harder than nails the few times I spoke to my family. I feigned strength, blasting the song "I Don't Care Anymore" by Phil Collins almost daily. My anger kept me from falling apart. Once the baby was born, the dynamics settled down, and everyone was happy to have a beautiful baby join the family.

Post-partum blues

Our baby arrived when she was ready, with no induction, no Pitocin, no forceful pressure from hospital staff. It was a home birth, a five-minute drive from the same hospital where I was born. As beautiful as the birth was, nursing from day one was a total nightmare. No one in my family had experience with breastfeeding. I reached out for help from professionals, but the first eight weeks were pure confusion and misery. While I was determined to figure it out (as I was used to always doing), my post-partum depression and anxiety overtook me, and I drowned in a sense that I was failing miserably at mothering.

About a year or so after our girl was born, I started to identify my problems with anxiety which were at a fever pitch and impossible to ignore. Living in a house on the service road of the Cross Island Parkway, I could barely sleep between the sound and vibration of the cars on the highway and my man's heavy snoring. With chronic lack of sleep, endless days and nights of painful nursing, and no reprieve, I obsessed over baby carriers and feeding times. The communication with my baby daddy (we didn't marry until our girl was eight months old) about my incessant need to buy things illuminated how laser-focused I was on minutia while barely holding it together. In my mind, things would make me comfortable; people surely couldn't.

I missed working, so I went to work doing massage at a well-known franchise 15 minutes away shortly after her first birthday. It felt good to have an escape from motherhood and get out of the house. We started to visit his brother in Connecticut more and more often. It seemed a much better place to raise our daughter than congested and loud eastern Queens. Besides, it was about time for another geographical upheaval. The whole time we were making our plans to move north, I felt the relationship was leveling out, and we grew distant from each other. When we first got together, he quit smoking and drinking almost immediately. When I got pregnant, he returned to those habits almost as fast. He said he wanted to be healthier but used the circumstances as his "out" to live as he was used to—smoking and drinking much and often, telling me how stressful our lives had become for him. He started to spend more time in his man-cave garage, and his time alone left me feeling partnerless. Aside from wanting to be healthy conceptually, we had little in common besides our teenage romance. He wasn't interested in my mental, philosophical, or psychological wanderings, and I was bored by the constant TV shows that captivated him. Moving gave us something to look forward to.

My irritability and discontentedness only grew, and my presence continued to be fleeting as it always was. I worked part-time, making decent money, and mothered my baby girl happily at times. I felt little connection to my now-second husband. Again, my life lacked depth, and it started to bother me, as my life perpetually did. Opting out of a superficial life with the veterinarian somehow morphed into a shallow life with the machinist.

The messages from the Universe (or was it my insatiable ego?) told me I had more to do in this life, although I was clueless as to what it might be. I was being called to something, as I was displeased with my circumstances perpetually through nearly all my days. I had to obey this intense drive to move, exhaustingly, forward. I wanted a fulfilling life, and it always seemed just beyond my reach. After our move to Connecticut, nearing forty, I was certain that my current life was missing something. I started to wonder if maybe I was inconsolable. That mischievous Cheshire cat from Wonderland seemed to tease me onward.

"Keep going," he told me as he vanished into the woods.

Headed for a breakdown

Six months after we high-tailed it to Connecticut, I left my second husband. We were married for three whole years. When something doesn't feel right, I jet. That's how I rolled, and I was kind of proud of it. Working as a Licensed Massage Therapist (LMT) full-time and being a mom was beyond draining. I started writing poetry again, a lot of it to alleviate the stress of it all. Going out to open mics at local bars and coffeehouses served as a great escape from my mundane and depressing solo parenting life. I pretended to have it together, the best I could muster.

I managed to pay my bills almost every month. Feeling more isolated than I ever was before in my life, my daughter challenged me to my core. I couldn't run away from motherhood as I did with everything else before. I became aware of how rageful I was with her and sought some professional help. I knew there was no way that she, as a toddler, could be the problem in this situation. In therapy, I learned about accountability and owned my inability to deal with immensely stressful dynamics and had an outlet to cope with the grief of not having any solid support from family or friends. Lacking emotional support was becoming a more significant issue, and now it wasn't only me who was suffering. Still, I didn't have a clue how to receive support, let alone ask for it without guilt and shame. I felt trapped in my circumstances after chasing freedom for so long, I was still enslaved by my own restlessness.

At the dawn of my separation, the winter of 2014 launched my first "dark night of the soul." I was cornered between all my circumstances with nowhere to run or hide. Searching Google for answers, I looked up "gratitude prayers" hearing how thankfulness can help one feel better about their own life and that having gratitude grows more things to be thankful for. The following prayer from an unknown author really resonated with me because it was not all about pretending to be happy for what I had, but it taught to be thankful for the lessons that life teaches. Out of sheer desperation, I began to cultivate this gratitude practice every morning to manage my emotions and experience:

Be Thankful

Be thankful that you don't already have everything you desire,

if you did, what would there be to look forward to?

Be thankful when you don't know something,

for it gives you the opportunity to learn.

Be thankful for your limitations,

because they give you opportunities for improvement.

Be thankful for each new challenge,

because it will build your strength and character.

Be thankful for your mistakes,

they will teach you valuable lessons.

Be thankful when you are tired and weary,

because it means you've made a difference.

It is easy to be thankful for the good things.

A life of rich fulfillment comes to those who are

also thankful for the setbacks.

GRATITUDE can turn a negative into a positive.

Find a way to be thankful for your troubles,

and they can become your blessings.

Through this practice, I became more honest than I ever was before. I was stuck with my mucky feelings and learned to honor my life's messes. Before then, denial was my setpoint. Pretending I was ok while lying to myself and everyone else covered up all the pain I was carrying. Nowhere to run, I went inward deeply. This would be the first time I stayed there, and I didn't want to bolt. My shadow-self embraced me with a warm hug, and I initiated falling in love with it.

In the heaviness of my darkest time, I designed a format for a dance movement class for "those who hate to exercise." I created it for people like me, who were too exhausted and bogged down to get up and go. Creating this class made me feel hope for the first time in my life. The new habit of gratitude began a shift in me that took me to where I am now. My life changed for the better right around the winter solstice. The light of appreciation was that missing piece all along.

Stillness in Action

✓ List a small inventory of five to ten things and circumstances you appreciate exactly as they are now. Then make another small list of things and circumstances you wish were different. Ask yourself if you have control over each of those things. Make a note of each item you can control. Now, make a list of every item you cannot control (people are not things, by the way, so they must go on a different list). Take the list of things you cannot control, rip it into pieces, and throw it in the recycling bin. The list of people whom you cannot control needs to stay and rename the list to "People I need to accept exactly as they are."

✓ Then practice the art of acceptance by speaking these words silently to yourself or aloud: "Today, I will live in acceptance rather than expectation."

✓ Breathwork: Breathe in through the nose while confirming "I am acceptance." Breathe out through the mouth, confirming "I release expectations." Repeat a minimum of three times for as long as you like.

Action in Stillness

✓ Witness the thoughts and feelings that rose within you while practicing each of the actions, both during and afterward.

Action Initiative:

✓ Write yourself a reminder or put the gratitude practice into your smartphone to come up with five different things and circumstances you appreciate for seven days.

4

Lack to abundance.
Love beyond fear.
Victim to victor.
Freedom from enslaved.
This is the process, the journey
Witness and thrive.
Free to everyone, the blessed ones drawn,
exactly as you are.
Trust the process.
Feel the expansion in your view.

Chapter 4

Talking the Walk

"I was hoping that perhaps I could roll with you..."
"You cannot roll with me," said the Big O,
"But perhaps you can roll by yourself."
—Shel Silverstein, The Missing Piece Meets the Big O

My missing piece

During those frigid days of winter at the end of 2014, I learned to honor the good as blessings and the bad as lessons, to be thankful for it all. The dawn of creating my regular gratitude practice helped me move through a depression that I felt for decades but was too proud ever to validate. That winter, I noticed how my strength was running low. Except, I only knew how to pretend I was fine (Feeling Insecure, Neurotic, and Emotional!). In actuality, I was barely functioning. Another irresponsible economic incident (budget, what budget?) caused me to reach out for financial help from my family. My father was generous and bailed me out of yet another tight jam when the bills were just a bit more than my paychecks could handle. I always felt so ashamed for needing to ask for support. My relatives seemed shocked and appalled that I'd need financial help at my age. It was a humiliating time of life. Although I asked for money, what I really needed was emotional assistance. I just didn't know it at the time. I'd live this way for a couple of more years until I took the leap into self-employment and started my massage practice.

Being so broke all the time and excruciatingly isolated was the perfect time to learn to have an appreciation for everything I DID have that was good in my life. I had a place to live. I had a daughter. I had food to eat. I had running hot water and sanitation. I had a car. I had love in my heart and a desire to help others. I was doing the best I could and wanted to grow. I was learning how to identify and validate my feelings for the first time ever at forty. I stopped running away from my problems. My life had me cornered, I was stuck yet I knew it was a way to a new place I'd never traveled before. I had a sense that was all happening for good reason, even God's will, so I didn't resent any part of it. For the first time, I embraced where I was and allowed my life to take its course one day at a time.

Re-framing all that ever happened in my past through the lens of appreciation was the gift. All the old events became tools from which to develop from. Every challenge, every mistake taught me something. That winter, life opened up and became a school; outpouring only divine lessons everywhere I looked. The responsibility of motherhood anchored me precisely where I needed to be. It was overwhelming to absorb it all and took years to digest and get a grip on the influence of my new angle.

The pattern emerges

Even though my anxiety and depression still ruled me, I became aware of them. Now I was watching my runaway train and seeing how fast it was going. It was painful to acknowledge, but a relief to see my experience with a bit less reactivity and from a wider perspective. I was a single parent, working my ass off at an hourly earning job, physically exhausting myself for a halfway decent paycheck. Something about the struggle of this experience felt familiar, even though the situation was brand new to me. There's an old Chinese proverb that says "Each generation will reap what the former generation has sown." I was yielding what I had experienced in my childhood. Re-living my mother's struggle in a different form—as she re-lived her mother's battle with loneliness. When my daughter was nearing four years of age, I saw my mother's angry outbursts in me. I found a local "Positive Discipline" parenting class and an excellent therapist to help me grant my daughter an emotionally healthy mother figure and stop myself from passing down this unhealthy struggle-pattern to my daughter. I always wanted to be the mom I always needed and needed fresh input.

The parenting classes taught me so much and reminded me how my parents were taught so little of it. It seemed my parents' generation didn't think asking for parenting guidance was okay. Instead, they pretended to know it all and have all figured out. Before the Baby Boomer generation, it was socially acceptable for relatives or friends to call parents out on their failings; but now, the mere mention of constructive criticism can shatter relationships instantly. The days of having extended families chime in to support parents are long gone. Seeing how I was relating to my daughter; I knew I needed more support to get me out of my maladaptive ditch. My tendency for emotional dysregulation improved through my awareness, seeing how strongly influenced my daughter was by my own emotional state. The classes were humbling, as I cultivated an understanding of my feelings of powerlessness and inadequacy, providing me with repeated breakdowns that led to a multitude of key breakthroughs. I discovered how to witness my shortcomings and weaknesses through my daughter's eyes with more objectivity, compassion and curiosity.

Mothering her didn't suddenly become a walk in the park, but I was learning how to be better for everyone's benefit, and that's all I could hope for and muster up through that era of our lives.

It's wild how our kids mirror to us what we are to them. Even more fascinating and insidious is how we project our issues onto our kids. If parenting is done right, the parent-child dynamic is loaded with personal growth. In my parenting, I am always coming back to appreciation and acceptance. This practice removes the shaming tendency that frequently creeps in. As I healed the shame inside myself, I was able and willing to love my daughter with the presence she deserves. Parenting is a fascinating career. Its lessons are beyond rich. That is, with the proper awareness.

As much as I remember, parenting for my folks only seemed to be a huge burden and an afterthought. Because they were busy working and trying to hold their own lives together, there was little quality time spent with my brother and me. My dad was immersed in operating his company, and my mom was usually resting in bed when she wasn't working or on a date. Neither of them was very active. I remember walking a few blocks with my mom once, and she got winded. I always remember exercise being a huge chore for her. Perhaps it was in my genes to wear out and become inactive. Maybe it was my life choices, as all the distractions of life seemed to override my desire to do my old living room dance-offs as I did throughout my childhood and into my early teens. Back then, it was the way I stayed honest with my feelings, in dealing with all the moving parts of my chaotic family and ever-changing social life. Life took over and very gradually, adulting sucked the fun out of the notion of activity.

Hating exercise

At the tail end of 2014, in the new rental with a toddler, I got into using my cell phone as my best friend, sharing my thoughts and feelings through Facebook posts. Aside from my growing proclivity towards writing poetry, which was pouring out of me all throughout my separation with my daughter's father. Facebook was the main outlet for my isolation and the place where I would pontificate on social norms and air random and not-so-random grievances. I was one of those who was into sharing a bit too much while remaining vague and obscure enough to think it artistic as if I was some rebel poet living in a small town in Western Connecticut. I noticed how lazy I felt after work and wondered when I stopped dancing. The notion kept popping up more and more, and I started to dance again but felt very lethargic. Somehow, I was blocked from it. Letting off steam and emoting through dance was second nature to me until the wind slowly began to leave my sails. My vitality was getting pulled under by some unrecognizable force I'd later know as dis-ease. Since college, the neck pain and chronic headaches only grew in consistency and frequency. Little did I know, exhaustion was taking its toll on me, but I was amid my denial. I wasn't allowed to prioritize my pain. I had more important matters to concern myself with, like earning a steady paycheck, motherhood, and managing a lively social life to distract myself from all the pain I minimized.

Gabrielle Roth, an American dancer and developer of the practice of 5Rhythems said it perfectly:

> "In many shamanic societies, if you came to a medicine person complaining of being disheartened, dispirited, or depressed, they would ask one of four questions: "When did you stop dancing? When did you stop singing? When did you stop being enchanted by stories? When did you stop being comforted by the sweet territory of silence?"

Getting it straight

Aside from my new gratitude practice, my poetry was the only other activity that provided me some inward reflection. I began to share my poetry in public, and it became a great pastime where I started to make a couple of friends who were more like reporters and informants for a very exclusive local music community. I didn't fit in, and I felt it. I was over forty, crushing on a fiddle player who could've won an award for making a mockery out of me. An idealized stranger distant enough to obsess over, the humiliation was non-stop and I kept coming back for more. He'd give me hope of meeting up, only to leave me hanging time after time. Once in a while, he would grace me with his presence and spend hours arguing with me why we would never work. I sought distraction, and he was the perfect procrastination tool, my personal energy-vampire. The great escape from my life focus for longer than I care to admit. Mr. Fiddleman served his purpose, I learned so much about my own dysfunctional relating from someone who played me better than his violin.

Since I could no longer run away from my problems, I became entrenched in more convenient escapes from socially acceptable addictions. They were pop culture quick fixes like drinking at local bars watching open mic talent shows once or twice a week. Except for cannabis and a couple of dating apps, Facebook and Instagram were my most intimate companions, keeping me feeling I had fullness in my strange and isolated little world. I dug in harder to these distractions, clinging to that habit of escaping the present moment and my greater responsibilities for dear life. Due to fear and deep insecurities, I had massive resistance to focusing on my life's purpose. The distractions were overwhelmingly convenient. Add a copious amount of codependency, and poof, avoidance abounded!

Planting seeds, making roots

I got the desire to start dancing more in my living room, but I still kept feeling a block of some kind and wasn't creative in my physical expression like I used to be. I came up with an alignment technique called "rooting-up," which felt good to grow better posture and body awareness. I loved helping myself with my posture and confidence while also helping others who struggled with the same issues of pain and poor self-image. In my tinkering with the alignment focus, it struck me to create a straightforward dance format for people too tired to exercise and incorporate the rooting-up posture alignment method. The routine was so effortless that you didn't have to think hard about what was coming next, and the format followed a logical flow. The phases of the class started to create themselves. Coming up with fun phrases and names of positions was like a joyful puzzle. I kept playing with it and practicing. I felt great afterward, like I'd actually finished a real exercise class, but only actual fun was had! By spring, I came alive with the deepest urge to share the program I'd developed. I was both excited and terrified! Oddly, I also had a feeling that's how it's supposed to go with a new idea.

After teaching my newly founded movement class at local churches in my spare time, I then taught it at a couple of small yoga studios in and around town. Participants were few, but they all seemed to get a lot of enjoyment out of the experience. After most people completed my unique brand of low-impact exercise, they raved about being uplifted and feeling more energized. Maybe it could have taken off then, but at the time, I didn't know how to stay focused on my purpose. Everything else in my life seemed to be more important and less overwhelming than launching a start-up exercise program. I quickly fizzled out. Running on steam with negligible support and lacking in boundaries, I simply wasn't able to keep it going. My own saying of, "moving the movement," wasn't as easy as I hoped.

Try, try again

Between work, motherhood, and my artificially maxed social life, my bandwidth was so slim. I was drained by the end of my first year of teaching the class I called Intuitive Movement. I didn't realize it then, but my heavy focus on external aspects drained all my energy, mainly my social endeavors and dating life. Instead of moving locations, I escaped with excessive social indulgences and nonsensical distractions.

At the time, I believed the classes were draining me, but my insecurities and fear were actually siphoning my drive to commit fully to teaching classes. I doubted that Intuitive Movement was what I was supposed to be doing with my life. I felt judged by people in the "real" exercise world, and yoga folks seemed unenthusiastic even to give it a try. My self-doubt repelled the people I wanted to attract. Subconsciously creating a storm of chaos around the dream of sharing it, I backed down. Yet it kept coming back to my mind. Something was telling me I had to teach this class. I knew if I put it down and never looked back, I'd regret it for the rest of my days.

Before I started back up again, I decided I needed more tools to learn how to be a better instructor. I knew the training would help my confidence, credibility, and ability to teach the best I could. I got my certificate in group fitness with the American Fitness and Athletics Association on my daughter's fifth birthday. It definitely helped, and I began teaching again, but my lack of focus on it continued—as did my fears and my incredible ability to distract myself with my social endeavors. The tendency to obsess on minutia kept weakening my resolve. It was as though I was averted from my own purpose, a fear of my own destiny. Alternately, my codependency, i.e., the need to belong to a group and find love, persisted. I had a vast emptiness in my heart, and it kept me from what I believed was my calling. Everything and everyone else were more important for some unidentifiable reason. Something was blocking me from diving in; that thing was wrapped up in one word—fear. My faith in myself was nil.

I wondered how to reach people like myself, too self-conscious to exercise at the gym. I hated the gym experience, the lights, the awkward social interactions, the energy of the big egos. Something about it was so unnatural. I felt like I was in a glass cage on a hamster wheel on display. All of it was too stimulating for me. Gyms were a little open to my class, but my judgmental and repelling energy sabotaged that too. I wanted to inspire those too exhausted to lift a dumbbell to try Intuitive Movement as a more fun and straightforward way to get moving. I envisioned my class being a gateway to exercise; as a preparation for getting physical activity into people's lives in a kinder, more gentle way than jumping into the gym fishbowl.

The people I was trying to reach were fatigued, unmotivated, and self-conscious, just like me. Finding how to connect with them was like a riddle, and I couldn't figure out the answer. I couldn't reach or teach them because I wasn't "there" yet. I had to figure out how to get past the paralyzing self-consciousness to lead. It was impossible to teach being an unhealed codependent! I had to be free of it in order to teach and I was nowhere near there at this point. I had to develop the leadership by healing myself first. Learning this was painful. I taught myself confidence and better internal focus by practicing my class solo. This "exercise" gave me hope that I was on the right track. After all that speculation, there was no riddle I had to solve, all I had to do was heal my own relationships, especially the one with myself, reaching others would just happen naturally from that point. That is how the power of attraction works.

Progress, not perfection

Somewhere around 2018, I changed the name to the Intuitive Movement Integration (IMI) experience. It ceased to be a class; instead, I marketed it as a group experiential inward journey. It is an embodiment practice, not a course. So much more than a mere dance movement class, it teaches the foundations of healthy posture I'd been training myself in since I started to learn posture exercises at my first chiropractic visit at the start of massage school back in 2009. Posture is more meaningful than just how we sit and stand. It holds our self-worth, attitude towards the world, and beliefs about ourselves. IMI is educational, simplistic, and fun. It can be a bit weird, as all new things are. Something about it is so bare-bones and straightforward. The IMI method has no fluff, not an ounce of it. It is child-like in its simplicity and yogic in its spirituality.

IMI is intended for two kinds of people: perpetual beginners who keep on starting and never maintain physical activity and people who enjoy dancing. In fact, IMI can show people who think they can't dance that they can. It gives folks permission to explore and enjoy the fumbling nature of freeform dancing. The IMI Experience is an intimate, self-focusing internal event, but it is also frivolous and fun, taking place among a kind-hearted group. The IMI Experience is like a new friend, a bit shy and awkward at first, but as comfortable as a t-shirt once you get to know it.

Created for people who suffer from chronic fatigue and pain, the method came out of my physical pain and my determination to eliminate it. I knew I was blocked, but couldn't recognize what it was, until hindsight, after I learned more about myself. If only I could get out of my own way. IMI ultimately became the experience that enabled me to do just that.

Stillness in Action

- ✓ Observe what pain and emotional discomfort you minimize because you are too busy to tend to it?

- ✓ Consider ways to resolve or accept the pain and discomfort if you can. If you aren't sure, be aware of that and its impact on your relationship with it.

Action in Stillness

- ✓ Notice if there are any modifications to your life that you may want to make to create more time to ease your pain and discomfort.

Challenge

- ✓ Visualize having the time and energy to rectify any pain and discomfort you've acknowledged. What resources are there to support making that a reality? Are they available online? Search for resources online and see what avenues exist for resolving your pain, and be open to new solutions.

- ✓ Journal about your possible paths to explore how to solve or accept the discomfort in your life. Confide in a friend or professional with your findings.

5

Sick of it
They stopped selling cigarettes
Too blatant was the contradiction
Ciga-butts and Nicorette
Shan't be sold by the same outfit

Why stop there?
To the front to get the daily things
To the back when they make you sick

Poetry piece, Sick of It

Chapter 5

Getting Schooled

"Listen to your body, it's smarter than you."
—Unknown

Backtracking to 1995

When earning my bachelor's degree at Binghamton, I started to get an increase in the frequency of headaches and neck pain, sometimes migraines, and sometimes tension headaches. I wasn't ever sure of their origin or type, and I never made a big deal of them, even though I suffered from them on a regular basis. I figured the neck pain was just due to the stress of schoolwork. I had headaches throughout grade school, middle and high school and it was pain I had gotten used to. They seemed to be worsening and also much more constant during my college years. Debilitating and incapacitating, all I could do was shut the lights and sleep it off, which usually worked but sacrificed a lot of productivity time, especially during mid-terms and final exams. I sought relief from herbal remedies and massage, which gave little lasting relief. Having a natural curiosity about herbs and a strong aversion and desire not to abuse over-the-counter pain meds, this was where my very long journey of searching for the root cause of my pain began. I felt embarrassed the first time I stepped foot into a health food store, asking a clerk to help me treat my pain. Nothing I tried ever really helped, but I became curious about what was causing them. I knew, innately, there was a reason for them and I was determined to solve the mystery. My head and neck pain were only starting to ramp up.

The pain pattern continues

In reluctance, knowing how toxic non-steroidal anti-inflammatory drugs (NSAIDs) were to my digestive system, I felt powerless and submitted to regularly taking pain relievers a few times a month, weekly, and sometimes for days in a row. My affliction only intensified as the years passed. By 2008, the headaches were happening three or four times a week. I worked for a small solar-electric company as a marketing assistant, living my seemingly picture-perfect conformist life and about to marry the veterinarian. That massage school down the road was calling my name. My suffering was the main draw to heed the call of becoming a massage therapist, an idea that originated back in 1999 while in Mendocino. I wanted to learn how to give others what I could not find for myself—relief from the chronic suffering of pain. I loved the idea of the serene environment and the peace I would provide people as an LMT. At the time, I had no idea this desire was also related to being a certified people-pleaser. It boggled my mind that there were massage therapists who didn't seem to listen when I explained my suffering, practically begging them to focus on my head and neck to help me relieve my headache. A good massage was hard to find. So, I sought to be the person who provided exactly what I ached for. I'd be a massage therapist who cared deeply about my clients' pain. Little did I know my empathy and finely-tuned nervous system would take my work in a completely different direction.

The physical pain in massage school was relentless. Although I was mesmerized by my class content, I had headaches and neck pain by the end of most of my school days. Plus, my lower back was starting to act up too.

Running out of options

Since Binghamton, I had avoided the idea of a chiropractor, dreading that cracking sound, fearing they'd accidentally break my neck or cause some other irreversible damage. At this point, I was entirely desperate for relief and solutions to this debilitating chronic pain. All I wanted to do was fix whatever was broken in me. What was broken reached beyond physical pain, there were more than a few factors to its symptoms.

The body speaks louder

Clearly, my body was sending me a strong message that something was not ok. The chiropractor sent me for x-rays after my first visit. As soon as he walked me into the small private office, pulling up the prints of my neck, he asked me something that shocked me.

He asked, "What happened to YOU?"

I was stunned.

He pointed to three vertebrae at the lower aspect of my neck and told me that there had to have been some physical trauma. He said, "You have bone degradation right here that's equivalent to an 80-year-old woman. Clearly, you were in some kind of accident." Confused by his interrogation, I drew a blank, which wasn't really so unique. My response was usually to freeze when confronted with blunt questions from authority figures. I had no idea what had happened to me that caused the injury. *It took me a full year to recollect what transpired to cause the damage.* That old memory popped into my mind vividly and out of nowhere.

Some trauma

At Robin Hood Country Day Camp back in 1981, they weren't big on accident reporting. There was no exception to the rule the day I was catapulted from a horse as we were slowly going around and around the circular track on horseback. My flimsy excuse for a helmet flew off my head, and I only remember looking at it as I woke up lying on the ground next to it. I have no idea how long I was lying there. Did I lose consciousness? Of course, like every other mishap and incident of negligence in my childhood, I shrugged it off and believed I was fine. And so did the camp counselors.

This could explain why I cringed every time I saw neck injuries as if they were happening to me. In fact, it did happen to me and my body never forgot. For some reason, my mind suppressed the memory. That's how traumatic injuries often play out. In Bessel Van Der Kolk's New York Times bestseller, "The Body Keeps the Score," he explains the phenomena of blanking out from traumatic events. In explaining how a patient's "mind went blank," and that "dissociation (is common) in response to being reminded of past trauma." I don't remember telling my mother the day it happened—or ever. I completely forgot about it. Perhaps the reason for all of it was to tell the story. God only knows.

Validation, finally

It felt amazing to have a source and origin of my pain after so many years of being in the dark. The chiropractor explained that studying with my neck angled downwards aggravated the issue and demonstrated some posture exercises to help me practice re-alignment. He told me to keep my head on top of my body and avoid sticking it out ahead of the rest of me. (I lived ahead of myself, figuratively, so that made complete sense.) He advised that I use book stands and quit bending my head down to read. With those suggestions alone, my headaches started to lessen in their frequency, which gave me a lot of hope and inspiration. Having the promise of pain relief simply from adjusting my body mechanics a little, I started to practice the art of putting my head on top of my body as often as possible. By the end of massage school, I was having about half as many headaches as when I started.

Curious to learn more about the trauma in my neck, I wanted to see what a traditional orthopedic surgeon thought about my old neck injury. Dedicated to his disposition to recommend invasive surgical procedures, he told me that neck surgery was inevitable for me. He also went out of his way to mock the massage profession, saying that too many people who "need" surgery are led astray by massage therapists like me, delaying or preventing their procedures. How dare his patients to question the need for surgery, right? Understanding how it cuts into his profits, I was so angry with his position and set out to prove him wrong. I'd not ever need surgery, I thought to myself. My neck can heal, I believed. Shortly after that, I had an MRI done to see what intricacies would be revealed in my cervical spine (my neck). It showed herniations, bulging discs, and bone spurs from C4-C7. Answers felt amazing, and now I actually had something specific to focus on fixing. Humbling it would come to be, that my body has its own timeline for healing, and my own habits had much to do with that timeline. Full recovery of a significant neck injury was unrealistic, but at the time, it didn't really matter. Pain management would need to enter my field of vision after a better understanding of the constraints of physical healing of chronic conditions.

I thought fixing it was the only solution to end my pain. I hoped that there would be an end to my suffering. In time, I learned that pain is a part of life, and there's importance in accepting that pain is necessary before creating any changes. Turns out that what we do with our pain messages matters most. Everyone has pain of some kind, how we deal with our pain makes all the difference to the quality of living it.

Pain is a language; our task is to get the messages contained in it. Legendary yogic guru Ram Dass addresses the approach to pain and the potential impact it has on our lives, stating, "You can do it like it's a great weight on you, or you can do like it's a part of the dance."

Where pain and meaning meet

The more I worked with alleviating my pain, the more my hunger for knowledge increased. Understanding the purpose of pain would forever affect how I related with my clients in supporting their pain-relieving strategies off of the massage table. I hung on to the wisdom conveyed by many instructors. Once a teacher once announced, "The issue is in the tissue," it left me mesmerized. It felt like the world's mysteries were opening up to me in massage school.

Connecting how my traumatic neck injury's locale was point-blank at the throat chakra, the energy center of expression and communication, was markedly poignant. The chakra system was introduced to me in school without much detail. Energy work was entirely over my head at the time. It would take me another two decades to bridge the connection between my childhood injury and the limitations of my communication skills. Unbeknownst to me, they were hijacked by my predominant emotion of fear. Thanks to a chance fall from a horse, I had a fundamental physical block in healthy communication. The depth of it all was fascinating to me.

During massage school and beyond, I made my posture exercises a habit, training myself to keep my head on top of my body and taught myself not to slump, staying "rooted" on my sitz bones (ischial tuberosities, on the very bottom of the pelvis), which aligned my entire spine so I could sit with less pain and fewer headaches. I started to prefer this position, and better posture began to feel natural over the months and years.

Turning up the heat

Although my headaches were fewer, there was a distinct cause of continuing to have them. And the "flare-ups" of my arthritis would be caused by cortisol production (brought about by chronic immense emotional stress) as well as the consumption of certain inflammatory foods. An arthritic flare-up is inflammation, an immune response to irritation. For over five thousand years, Traditional Chinese Medicine has called that inflammation "excessive heat" in the body. That's logical, but there's so much to what causes tissues to become hot. Talk of inflammation and anti-inflammatory diets was a huge topic in the wellness field during the new millennium's first decade. Naturally, I obsessively dove into all I could learn about it. There exist many triggers of an overproduction of inflammation in the body; mental and emotional stress, certain foods, drugs and alcohol, sleep deprivation, and fluctuating hormones to name a few.

From a simplistic perspective, I repetitively viewed a lot of my life's happenings as burden and a real "pain in the neck." My family relationships were uncomfortable and stressful, and most of my waking hours were lived on a spectrum of varying intensities of fear for as long as I could recall. The more I learned about the different meanings of my pain, the further down into the rabbit hole I fell.

Pain and the great escape

The pain and emotional upset led me to an awareness of my patterned ingratitude in 2014 by practicing appreciation every morning. Subconsciously, I had been groomed for perpetual dissatisfaction and disappointment that looped throughout all my days. Birthed into a consciousness of hyper-criticism, control, perfectionism, and inadequacy breeds a seemingly benign variety of thanklessness that fuels the consumerism of the day. I spent so much money trying to fill the void of contentedness I craved.

Consumerism runs on that void in people! Buying things, eating things, smoking and drinking things kept me feeling safe in a world of continually unsatisfying relationships.

It appears all the dysfunction of the modern world has gone under the radar so long as we humans keep on filling the void in lieu of repairing broken and toxic relationship dynamics. Personally attesting to my filling the void with social media, prowling for love, drinking alcohol, smoking cannabis, snacking on crap foods, shopping for all the things all too often, only to feel worse after the high of filling wore off. Giving up all of these things was a process in and of itself. It took some frustration and a lot of time and awareness.

Counting the blessings

What led to greater fulfillment was unlearning ingratitude and looking for aspects to be thankful for. It also stopped the hamster wheel of disappointment and insatiability. Appreciation was the antidote to my addictions and avoidances of managing my chronic pain and emotional discomfort. I found the way out of my own madness by learning to re-frame the emotions of sadness, anger, resentment, frustration, grief, jealousy, rejection, and pain into normal human occurrences, taking the sting out of my suffering.

The ego is destined to be dissatisfied. It wants what it wants and will do anything to justify its compulsions and desires. Its job is to prepare for the future, referencing the past to prevent reoccurring problems. Paradoxically, the ego only attaches us to outcomes that can never fully satisfy us and ones that resemble the past on some level or another. The ego does not live in the present moment. Yet we are only ever satisfied when we live in the present moment. Before the ego aspect of our personality takes over, we live in the thankful present. The ego dies with every conscious breath taken. Presence is an invaluable and priceless gift, and we cultivate it with conscious breath. Sounds easy, right? The only hard part is when we judge those darn heavy feelings that surface to be recognized and dealt with.

Speaking the language of wellness

I knew I was on my path to wellness, but I hobbled on it begrudgingly. Presence was only starting to sprout in me, in my early forties. At the same time, I fought the giant demons of low self-esteem, crippling codependency-related anxiety attacks, and don't forget my many maladaptive coping mechanisms, i.e., addictions of the most socially acceptable kind. I still had much healing to do before sharing all I learned with anyone else. Not knowing I didn't know how unhealed I was, I kept trying to "get myself out there," promoting myself as a fitness instructor of my own making.

I gave what I needed and still wasn't getting myself. That was the lens of my service work. Talk about being needy; my service was enmeshed in my growth. I wanted to make a living helping others feel better, and I wanted to feel better too. It was an "all ships rise together" theory. The trouble is that no real leadership can be had without first mastering the ease of a confident presence. That's the secret sauce. I knew I was onto something big, but I also lacked the most important ingredient touting wellness; self-love. This self-loving energy was buried underneath my big ravenous ego, poor coping mechanisms, and escapism and needed to be unearthed.

The dirty work lies right there. I was starting to dig into the dirt becoming aware of how much love I lacked for myself. The path to emPOWERment is not pristine as so many believe; that's for shit-sure. It was painful, but not as painful as my denial of what was. This digging was necessary for me to get myself genuinely free and emBODY my wellness.

Life lessons from massage school

I was in love with my massage school education. Half of my study hours were dedicated to TCM theory and practice. I loved how my school taught both clinical and eastern perspectives. They were both necessary and relevant to balanced health and well beingness. One teacher summarized it well, noting that Western medicine was best applied when "the shit hits the fan" (aka acute injuries, crises, and emergency care), while Eastern medicine was to "prevent the shit from hitting the fan" (aka chronic dis-ease, restorative, and protective care). Both achieve homeostasis, but Western medicine does not address the root causes or consider the body as one interwoven system. Instead, it's excellent at treating physical parts, "fixing" or numbing symptoms, and sometimes wreaking more havoc in the process. The symptoms are resolved as Eastern medicine searches for the energetic sources and treats it. Functional medicine is now illuminating the relationship between the two schools of thought, introducing the next paradigm of mainstream healthcare.

The body works miraculously, healing itself automatically when nothing obstructs the healing process. When we get a paper cut, it tears into the skin, making it bleed, forming a scab, and slowly growing new skin. The entire body is designed to heal the same way. That is, as long as we don't keep putting dirt in the wounds. Referred to in TCM as "insults," the "dirt in the wound" represents aspects that hinder healing within the body. Certain substances and behaviors are insults to recovery: stimulants will block calmness, sugar and snack foods will hinder weight loss and vitality, casual sex will impede self-love, and lack of movement will perpetuate lethargy. It's like, surrounding yourself with pollution and expecting clean air. Insults stop healing potential in its tracks and eventually cause damage. Too many verbal insults harm in the same way that excessive damaging inputs will create dis-ease. Normal functioning can't happen with too many insults! Now, to get onto the business of removing insults. Easier said than done, most folks like to add things and not take them away. Substituting one thing for another will suffice. Deprivation is a big problem for people, as it almost instantly brings up our emotional discomfort. Pain avoidance is how we got into this mess after all.

Anatomy, Nerves & Hormones

Massage education helped me understand how the human body's synchronous functions work. Why don't they teach this stuff in high school? *Is our collective wellness illiteracy serving to benefit something?* Can't help but wonder why health education is minimized in this culture where we are the least healthy on the planet compared to other nations.

I conveniently created another crisis while learning how the nervous system worked in massage school. Knowledge of the nervous system fascinated me, but I didn't recognize how most of my life was spent in "fight or flight" mode, the sympathetic aspect of the Autonomic Nervous System. Rarely was my nervous system in the parasympathetic state of "rest and digest." Whenever I did feel calm, I quickly snuffed it out with a hypervigilant vengeance. Safety was not a familiar sensation, looping in stress was.

It's no wonder the massage profession spoke to me. I was subconsciously calling out to learn how to rest my overwhelmed nervous system. Those hunches of the subconscious are ingenious; if only the ego was less noisy, I may have heard them sooner.

All my suppressed emotional energy drove this obsession with body knowledge and understanding. I had high expectations for not only myself, but for whoever was in my proximity. Perfectionism fueled my overactive and ultra-sensitive nervous system. No one was good enough for me, including me. From anxious highs to depressive lows, the hormonal roller-coaster was beginning to take its toll. Insomnia would be just the beginning of symptoms of my exhausted stress response.

One thing leads to another

That first chiropractic appointment was divinely timed. It set my path to discovering my purpose and self-actualization. Hot on the trail of healing my pain, my intention of serving others with pain-relieving massage was not just for the purpose of massage alone. I was more interested in helping people illuminate and resolve their root causes. Not that anyone asked or cared. This approach did not exactly win me much favor with the many clients who merely wanted to lose themselves in a nice rubdown. I had a ton to learn about boundaries. In fact, I didn't know what boundaries were until I had to enforce them professionally. No one ever taught me what boundaries were before. I projected my desire to fix my own pain problems onto my clients. I unknowingly stepped into my massage career as a "fixer," not a massage therapist. I confused massage with healing, another projection. I believed and assumed everyone else wanted what I wanted and saw through the same lens. Blind to my own self-absorption, it cost me a few clients who grew tired of my trying to get them to care about healing their chronic pain. I had no idea how pushy I was, as controlling people often are.

Fatal flaw perhaps, but a vital step toward my true purpose of wellness education. When I synced up with clients who wished me to fix them, it either gained me serious client loyalty or imploded with disappointment and frustration. You win some, and you lose some. Eventually, I learned to provide massage only and shut my yap. I learned to offer advice when asked for it. Beautiful lessons of boundaries would flourish in my career and push my inner growth further forward.

Because I had so much more to share, I wanted to offer more than massage. I saw myself as a healer as I emerged from massage school and worked out in the world. Oh, the plight of the wounded healer with much to learn about herself, her pain, and the world of healthy boundaries.

Deeper into dynamics

Encountering continual traumatic enmeshment dynamics in childhood kept me replaying the tape of enmeshed relating and then discarding relationships. I began to notice it in my relations with many clients. Some people were unsatisfiable, others had stoic walls and could not let themselves relax. New client experiences were unpredictable. Most were somewhere in between, just enjoying the experience of a good therapeutic massage. I remember feeling guilty, taking on personal responsibility for whatever pain I couldn't release in new clients. This wore me out after a while, but I was clueless as to why I felt so drained after interacting with certain folks.

However unconscious, it's common to over give and take on more responsibility that is rightfully ours. Takers seek out over givers and expect nothing less. In more relationships than realized, often someone is the master or dominant leader while the other is the slave or submissive follower. I know it may sound a little kinky now, but the power play is an essential key in dysfunctional relationships.

Having lived through so many, the lack of fulfillment in codependent-based relationships is the cause for all the betrayal, disappointment, and lovelessness. This is true for all relations, not just romantic but also familial, friendships, and professional ones too. It seems to be the root of all evil, unhealthy relating leads to imbalanced health. Having met my personal threshold of emotional pain, I thank it for the drive to my awareness. Pain serves its purpose, delivering consciousness in stopping the pattern of dysfunctional dynamics and psychological and physical boundary violations.

What caused my pattern interrupt was in through painful observation, of the repetitiveness of feeling uncomfortable and inconsolable; a vague but chronic state of uneasiness, with myself and in most of my relationships. The ancient Greek philosopher, Plato nailed it when he said, "Necessity is the mother of invention," and the necessity, in my case, was validating the emotional pain and creating some relief from it. In understanding my codependent thinking and behaviors I could learn to do something different—what a novel idea.

The constant external focus of finding a cure for my physical pain and hoping my emptiness would be filled by others kept me oblivious to my lack of love and respect for myself. Mutual respect begins with self-respect. The foundation of psychologically safe connections with other human beings begins with the belief that one is worthy of being treated well. That belief is learned—or not learned—early on in development. Worthiness was one of those lessons I missed out on until much later in life. As my awareness closed in on these dynamics in my early forties, I got schooled on the topic, in a sublime and karmic sort of fashion. The teachings came at exactly the right time and I learned those important lessons, painstakingly. Relationships are the foundation of how we contextualize ourselves. To recalibrate how we relate, we realign our whole essence.

Leaving again and again

Two months after I left my first husband, my pregnancy shocked my system, with less than a year left of massage school. Being "knocked up" at 38 at that exact juncture in time naturally was an outrage to my family. Who could blame them? My situation was pretty juicy and dramatic. It reflected the light of my desire to live differently than the expectations society was trying to coerce me into. Part of me wanted to fit in, yet my actions screamed otherwise; the bellowing was coming from my womb loud and clear. Finishing up school was interesting, with my belly getting heavier and heavier. My baby daddy and I decided to plan our departure from Queens for a better, calmer life in Western Connecticut and be closer to his family. At the same time, I was happily leaving my shaming family behind, at least geographically. The rift with them was irrevocable. I began to accept it. Finding myself packing again, it was getting old, and so was I.

I didn't realize it, but I was totally neurotic before my daughter was born, but my neuroses became noticeable to me afterward. I felt emotionally isolated, sleep-deprived, and the lack of deep intimate closeness depressed me, not that I ever had those things before. I felt unfulfilled and pretended motherhood was as joyful as I could. There were a few fleeting moments of elation in play, but the majority of my days left me anxious and melancholy.

With our baby in tow, doing our darnedest to be a new family unit, our move to CT was pretty smooth and primarily mechanical. He seemed to be ok with our lack of emotional intimacy. While I craved intimate connection, I had no clue how to articulate what I needed. I wanted to speak from my heart and tell him how scared and inadequate I felt. I wanted to voice my feelings, but I was always taught to shut them down instead of feeling welcome to express them. My emotion festered underneath the surface for as long as I could take it. This time, my ability to run away was undoubtedly disabled because of my daughter. She anchored me in more than one way. The patterns were all too obvious to me now, finally. I knew if I tried to run away and start over someplace else, I'd only re-create the same frustrations elsewhere. There was no way I was going to distance her from her father. She had a right to him, however imperfect he was. Besides, I had nowhere else to go. All I knew was I had to leave him. If he wasn't around, my problems would magically be solved...at least, that's what I told myself.

Impactful motherhood

I had fantasized about my own motherhood here and there at times in my life. I always wanted to be one, but the opportunity never presented itself until by accident at 38. I knew that, someday, when it was time for me to be a mother, I'd parent very differently from how my mother mothered me. I knew on a soul level that I'd break the ancestral legacy of abiding by social pressures and ignoring my intuition. My daughter wouldn't be coerced into hugging people she didn't want to. She would be allowed to eat until full, and never had to "clean her plate." She could do her own hair and pick out her own clothes. I'd not treat her like a doll or a mini-me. I would allow her to become whatever she wanted. Her life is hers, not mine to manage. I only wanted to foster her growth so that she could fulfil her own dreams and desires. The mother is their daughter's first and most important role model, what a huge honor and responsibility. Other role models can and often do substitute for a mother, as my aunt was for me, not that she signed up for the job. On paper, I carefully considered what I wanted to teach my daughter, but as life played out, my subconscious unresolved issues would surface to be healed. Now, the stakes were higher, it was about my child, not only me.

Again, being clueless about how profound motherhood would be for me, it was the greatest blessing of my life, and my daughter would become my most impactful teacher. Because she reflected what I needed to learn to be the best role model I could be, I still call her my "little Buddha."

My challenge was to prevent her from becoming a people-pleasing automaton like I was. I figured if I could facilitate her bravery, my job as a mother would be a great success. Undoing cultural programming of mothering is difficult, especially while unraveling the effects of my own—compounding it was the fact that I had a no blueprint for attentive mothering.

The career climb

Starting self-employment in 2016 seemed to be the only way out of scraping by my low-wage-earning life. Investing my time and energy into a Groupon campaign that paid my revenue bi-weekly supported quitting my full-time job at the massage chain, bridging me to the next chapter of my career. It was *the* most stressful time ever professionally while having a toddler to raise at home most days of the week. I was learning to rely on variable income without any financial security whatsoever. I began reinventing my business over and over.

Instead of teaching my IMI classes locally, I designed an educational presentation, by framing out the posture and body-mechanics concepts, and began to speak at libraries and small local businesses. Sharing my Posture & Body-Mechanics Workshops felt good. I felt a real career in the making. Talking in front of a group about what fascinated me was fun and exciting. Yet, there was a piece to health I overlooked that was calling out for some attention.

The nutritional component of physical alignment needed to be spoken to, since energy levels are vital to feeling well and all. I needed to get more education on the topic. At the time, I was healing my intimate relationship with my kitchen, trying to nourish myself more with healthy foods, not knowing exactly what they really were. The high-fat craze glorified fats now and shunned sugar and processed carbohydrates. This keto-like approach resonated with me, having two grandparents with diabetes. I felt signs of my genetic predisposition for it in my cravings and insatiable appetite when I'd start to indulge in those things. As I meandered through the confusing maze of nutritional health, I began to eat more fat from animal protein and minimized sugar and carbs, unless, of course, there was some pressing temptation that called. I was big on non-deprivation. The provocative world of eating well was overwhelmingly conflicting, and I was committed to sort through it.

I made some time taking an online course in nutrition coaching through the National Academy of Sports Medicine (NASM) to make sense of things. They had a well-rounded program with the most recent, statistically-significant scientific evidence for nourishment designed to support both advanced athletes and novices.

After I had a broader perspective of nutrition, I took my work into the trenches of the corporate world and became an ergonomics and wellness consultant, offering full-spectrum health education including the three main aspects of wellness; physical, mental, and emotional. My business life was starting to grow until it stopped abruptly when the world did too in early 2020.

Moving forward while locking down

The momentum came to a screeching halt. Like so many, I believed I could not break; I could not pause, or allow myself to feel weakness. The rise of COVID-19, would teach me otherwise. It was perfect timing for a needed disruption and a massive overhaul. The pandemic shut down the world, locking us in our homes for long enough to settle into our own skin—or die trying to escape ourselves. For me, it was a tug of war between the two on a daily basis.

Like most of the world, when it first struck, I went off the deep end in my addictions of comforting myself with sugar, snacking on processed foods, consuming alcohol and smoking cannabis. My insomnia was never worse, my fatigue was at an all-time high. I was sick of feeling so exhausted and decided to clean house. I shopped for healthy foods on Amazon gutted my cupboards of sugar, alcohol, and processed foods.

The caffeine and cannabis would stay. I wasn't convinced they were a problem. Then, a new skin rash and acne erupted on my left cheek in a funny shape. It's funny how it is when we are convinced we know what is good and bad for us when we really don't. The devil is in the details of nutrition, and eliminating basically everything under the expertise of a health team is the only path to health sanity instead of roaming the halls of nutrition unattended.

Facing it all

Until 2020, acne had never been an issue for me unless I ate greasy foods on occasion. If I went on a bender of sugars and alcohol (we're talking a typical portion here, not a binge-worthy one), I did notice a pimple or two, but never linked it to any inner workings that might be straining due to the influx of low quality, non-nutritive foods. My sugar and alcohol sensitivity got progressively worse. The stress of life was taking its toll on my body. I could never be the drinker others could, with a mixed sense of jealousy and thankfulness. One beer or glass of wine was giving me hangovers! Ice cream and French fries were starting to cause hangovers too. All through my young adulthood, I ate pretty healthily but indulged, like everyone else seemed to when there was some special occasion or opportunity to do so. Those special occasions are rather frequent, aren't they? There is always some important reason to give into unhealthy treats. "Just this once," "Only a little" are the words I hear when sugar calls, either from within or by a well-meaning food pusher. But the cravings continue for days until it's time to "get back on the wagon." And so, it goes—until the next special occasion arrives.

When this mysterious skin issue came up, I went to the dermatologist, and they gave me topical prescriptions to treat it. Nothing worked. I researched online and came up with my theories. I got the message from my body that something was going haywire but couldn't figure out exactly what. My primary doctor tested me for food sensitives and discovered plenty of them. We agreed I'd limit those foods (wheat, dairy, corn, and yeast were the worst offenders). My doctor suspected a leaky gut and was planning to give me antibiotics which I knew would only put a Band-Aid on the symptomatic issue, and not fix the root cause. At this point, my journey to resolve these worsening health issues only got murkier.

My skin would seem to be improving until I "fell off the wagon," uncontrollably indulging in my offending foods, which made the condition flare up again and again. This was the next pattern I was to become aware of; my actual addiction to sugar and processed foods. The root cause was no different from any other addiction; a trauma response to avoid emotional pain I did not feel safe to express.

Knowing no other way to figure it out, I was to find a way to eat cleanly and consistently on my own, as I did everything else. I prided myself on my self-reliance as though it was one of my greatest strengths. The thought never occurred to me that I needed help with my food addiction and would not be able to do it alone. If I only had the willpower, I thought, I could solve all of my health issues. Reaching out for help had always been a very negative, shame-inducing experience for me. I was consistently shut down and rejected when I vulnerably needed something my caregivers were unable or unwilling to provide. My needs were considered a pain in the ass. No real surprise to become someone to offer support to others. However, no one can give what they can't accept for themselves. It defies the laws of physics.

No one wins alone

That was the big block; not being receptive to getting the support I needed to stay accountable and feel the acceptance of others. Belonging was not something I was accustomed to. It was high time I learned.

Stillness in Action

- ✓ Write a list of all the physical and emotional pain of any kind you experience and note its perceived intensity. Describe the problems the pain introduces and jot down possible solutions or remedies.

- ✓ Go for a walk or do any physical activity of whatever length of time while contemplating each of your physical and emotional pain sites.

Action in Stillness

- ✓ Access how your pain feels during and after your activity.

- ✓ Imagine what you would do and how you would feel if your pain were less of a hindrance in your life.

- ✓ Observe your pain as if you were a scientist, without any attachment to it. No hating or resenting it, but instead, allowing it to be for a few minutes. What happened to the pain after you acknowledged and allowed it?

Action Initiative

- ✓ Be with your pain this week with compassion. Treat the pain as though it's a hurting friend who needs a little TLC.

6

This is a poem called Trust
My heart screams to those who delight in its howling
My soul churns inside these skin walls
It's safe now, come out and play

Poetry pieces, Trust

Chapter 6

Alignment Lessons

"Life speaks first in whispers. When we don't listen, the whispers get louder. Messages unheeded turn into problems and eventually crises. What's whispering to you now?"
—Oprah

With nowhere to go and feeling a bit like hell, I was lucky to have some time and space to process all the aspects keeping me in a holding pattern of less-than-ideal health. COVID brought invaluable teachings. I began to frame it all as a blessing in disguise. Eagerly feeding my mind with healthy-relationship education, I started healing from old trauma wounds. With fewer distractions of day-to-day life, it was quiet enough to validate needs and curiosities, resetting my perspective towards feeling emotionally honest and outgrowing the victimized mindset of my past.

The way to move forward is not to "let go" of the past. That merely dismisses its consequential effect, but to fully own it, process it, and unpack the why-it-happened and our actions and beliefs that contributed to the unfolding of events as they went down. Conceiving to accept the level of consciousness everyone (including ourselves) had at the time. Forgiveness is really acceptance at its core, which enables releasing it from our hearts, energetically. Perception can't be taken for granted here; our core beliefs are influenced by deciphering who's to blame for our pain. Such beliefs are passed through the generations until someone dares to re-examine these outdated beliefs and upgrade them into new ones. Self-responsibility, even if it's mere wrong-place-wrong-time, frees us from resentment. Acceptance upgrades our view of past emotional hurts and traumas. Much like software, humans function best when continually updating with new and updated downloads. These upgrades come with growing pains, but a good sort of pain, the pain of progress. There's no growth without pain, and no pleasure without feeling pain. When we stop denying pain pushing away discomfort, wanting to be something or somewhere else, resistance is removed and growth can flourish. Acceptance helps us not hate the lows and mellow out with the highs. Trouble is often how easy it is to avoid our pain and discomfort with all the distractions out there to self-soothe in gratuitous ways.

Appreciation aligns

The simple morning practice of saying aloud a list of dynamics to be thankful for cultivated a self-awareness so rich that all facets of my world began to take on relevance and meaning. People's behavior towards me grew more and more surreal and symbolic.

For as long as I could remember, I advocated against victim-mentality while living there intimately. Peeling back the layers of my victimhood felt endless, as any good spiritual journey is. Things were starting to get interesting as I found my way towards the notion of a greater purpose, all while practicing my physical alignment, not just once or twice, but all throughout my day and evenings as I sat and stood consciously.

Lengthening my neck, tucking my chin, sitting on my sitz bones, I reflected on sensations in my body and how my alignment helped me feel better inside my skin. I felt more present and more aware of my inner dialogue—the impact of learning to listen to my own body's messages created *inescapable accountability*.

Paradox of surrender

Refusing to admit my weakness was the obstacle to releasing my victimhood orientation. I frowned upon my exhaustion and weakness like any good American would. Self-reliant, I never needed anyone for anything and if I felt a desire for assistance, a sense of loneliness and self-pity would take me down hard. I was denied permission of having emotional support long ago. Asking for help in childhood was almost always met with rejection in some shape or form. After repeatedly getting a dismissive or non-existent response, you learn to stop asking and come to accept you have only yourself to rely on.

Just as COVID became rampantly airborne, I ran out of steam altogether. The strong woman I was, ceased to be. As I micromanaged my ongoing life-dramas with minimal support outside of my therapist, my emotional awareness steadily and slowly expanded. Instead of running away from my problems, I embraced them. There was a shift underway, being there for myself instead of fleeing to some substitute to focus on. A gradual progression, anything but neat and tidy.

Learning to deeply trust my reiki-master/wise-elder/nurturing role model of a therapist with my feelings took years prior to this. She was the gatekeeper I entrusted to tear down the walls of my self-isolation. Practicing sharing my deepest thoughts and feelings with another human being catapulted me into a breakthrough of safe vulnerability I'd never known before. We discovered this little girl inside me who schlepped all over the United States for someplace safe to dwell. Then she started to feel at home exactly where she was, in Western Connecticut. She always felt balled, alone, and left to her own devices. When I learned to comfort her and witness her pain, she started to open up and relax. I asked her to speak, gifting full permission to express herself without guilt or soul-annihilating condemnation. Listening quietly to whatever her heart had to say.

My anxiety began to wane through this introspective restoration work; my panic attacks dwindled over time. Little Lisa lives inside me forevermore. I am her parent now and she fully understands that I'm here for her exactly when she needs me. I'll never leave her again, now understanding my role. She had to be so patient, knowing I'd be ready someday to take good care of her by seeing, hearing, and understanding her needs, wishes, and beliefs.

Everyone has a child inside them that doesn't age. Releasing that pent-up energy is both lightwork and shadow work. Again, they are one and the same, two sides of the same coin of soul mending.

Shining the light on the little inner-kid who needs a little attention moves mountains.

The physics of projection

The wisdom of "Abraham," a collective consciousness channeled through the inspirational speaker, Ester Hicks, entered my life in the transition of my employment to self-employment. She articulated a vital law of physics called the Law of Attraction. Basically, that *we see what we believe* and not the other way around. Abraham, aka "God" or "Source energy," teaches that we manifest realities similar to what we think about and perpetuate whatever emotions (energetic resonance) we feel, however unconscious. Our minds and hearts send out vibrational signals that resonate with the outside world. It's a very controversial law and catches a lot of flak for seeming to blame people for their undesirable circumstances. People judging other's misfortune is of their own doing is not only insensitive, but minimizes the complexity of the subconscious mind. The Law of Attraction does not operate in a vacuum and should not be taken at face value for that reason. As hard as we try to rationally convince ourselves, this law of manifesting what realities we dwell upon has more to do with the playing of our subconscious reel deeper than our conscious awareness. Our thoughts may seem to lead our actions, but the subconscious aspect that are unaware of wants what it wants. More importantly, the subconscious gets what it expects. This aspect of our being pre-emptively rejects what we don't feel we can receive. The subconscious drives the phenomena of self-sabotage. Finding someone "out of your league" when you are strongly attracted to them, turning your eye away from them, afraid to smile at them is a case and point of the subconscious mind derailing a perfectly good intent. When there is no fear of rejection, a person would be free to make eye-contact and drum up a conversation. Believing is seeing, according to Hicks, and I fully concur.

Insatiably consuming her content for a few years reinforced the need to be thankful for all that came to me in life and all the emotions that go with it. I began to witness my own condemned emotions and feelings more and more just by slowing down my thoughts to follow the unfolding of events inside my body. Abraham spoke of the importance of the term "contrast," asserting that recognizing what isn't wanted in our lives reveals what *is* wanted. It's an elimination process of sorts. Through the concept of contrast, I understood that all undesirable events occurred to illuminate our preferences! Using our most unfortunate events as a strategic tool instead of seeing it as a curse, the more we experience what is undesired, the more we could discover our desires.

Being locked into my codependent nature, I never felt satisfied in relationships. There was a deep longing for closeness which I never was able to receive. Subconsciously, I didn't feel worthy of successful relationships, seeing what I believed. Observing this as a big pattern is exactly how I overcame it. Accepting my feelings of unworthiness liberated me from the cage that emotion locked me it.

Ester's teachings of Abraham would illuminate contrast in every facet of my life; finances, work, parenting, romance, and relations of all varieties. When Abraham spoke of taking full responsibility for one's circumstances, it blew my mind and forced me to learn about my shadowy penchant for disappointment and tendency to be a glutton for punishment. I was unaware of the victimized narrative I told my story from before Abraham's wisdom came into my life.

My problems were metaphysical, stemming from my long repressed, pent-up feelings, stale, and inaccurate beliefs created in childhood. All that I didn't want but kept saying yes to became glaringly obvious. My cognitive dissonance screamed at me now. By getting in sync with my inner guidance, life started to make more sense.

The most interesting contrast was among the distractions that came upon me all the time. Unconscious needs and repressed priorities drive these little machines of avoidance. At the dawning of my entrepreneurial career, my focus was on being a consumer and seeking approval from everyone else instead of my work. That fear of success drove my train until absolute necessity would make me take over the rails. Truth be told, tempestuous day-to-day distractions continuously show me what my priorities are. Like contrast, they are a blessing in disguise, showing me my preferences and subconscious desires. It reminds me of how the devil tempted Jesus to test his conviction. The allure of avoidance always beckons if we desire it in some way.

Moving energy

With all the contrast I was seeing, I felt overwhelmed by it all. Perhaps it could be labeled as a depressive phase of life. Labels of such mental and emotional experiences only infuriated me. It wasn't a mysterious depression. It made sense I was heavier than bricks, burnt out from strenuous physical and energetic work, exhausted from my over-active mind and emotionally demanding motherhood, while attempting to reach a purpose without any gas. For the first time, I would start to allow myself to feel feelings without judging them. This phase of growth took me to understand what energy work truly was all about. Before then, I didn't get it. Akin to Einstein's theory of relativity, E(motion)=Energy in Motion, and if it's not moving, it's building up somewhere in the body getting angry, agitated, and simmering, aka developing as inflammation and other dis-ease.

I took level one Reiki in massage school in 2010, along with twenty other students. In a basement room without windows, the miserable teacher was on the brink of quitting her job there after 20 years. Going through the attunement felt hokey and fake. I felt confusion as I allowed myself to be given symbols with my eyes closed, feeling hands moving in front of my body, seated, and doing my best to remain still. I didn't feel a thing shift after my "attunement." In 2017, was drawn back to Reiki energy healing, even though I didn't quite comprehend it. This time, it made more sense, at least logically. After having eight years under my belt of practicing massage and a lot of inner-growth, I understood and could better sense what energy was and how it worked. Still, I didn't connect with that knowledge on an intuitive level until my great burnout of 2020. Energy is not very mystical or spiritual, as we are led to believe. It's emotional at its core. And emotions have vibrations and resonance. Our instincts know damn well what energy is. Good or bad vibes attract or repel.

Chakras are ingenious symbols for emotions and aspects of human beingness. They are based on the physical body, but relate to the amorphous emotional body, which is all but written off in Western medicine. In its purest form, healing touch is energy work whether or not consciously aware of it. Touch is energetically transactional in a big way. Pure energy work is touch, and intention is the key to its message. I was providing energy work in my massages but not practicing reiki. Learning to receive proper reiki and massage moved so much of the emotion I was growing through at the time. After my second level one Reiki class, growth became my main focus as my emotional world became tangible.

Granting myself permission to feel my feelings was an indulgence I enjoyed, in all its exhaustion. I had license to be in my shadow, feeling feelings instead of feeling shame, guilt, and fear of them. The trust of my now long-term therapy enabled allowing myself to trust my own intuition fully. Funny how authentic validation works; inside, outside, microcosmic and macrocosmic. As above, so below, as within, so without. The power of mirroring by those who can be trusted, i.e., truth projection via reflection.

Knowing where to ask for help, check. Trusting the trustworthy, check. Lessons learned to move forward in my life, check.

Breaking the unworthiness spell

When others do not value us, we can become aware that we are somehow not loving ourselves. Wanting others to value us is an opportunity to see where we are lacking in self-love. Of course, others will not value you simply because you want them to. Still, our inherent worth of who we are is independent of anyone else's valuation. We all desire to be valuable, but if we don't feel worthy of being valued, we are stuck in a belief that we lack value. While this lack of value is mostly internal, the feeling and resonance of it is projected outwardly. Valuelessness is first learned by the way we are regarded. So, it's a belief that creates a lack of worth. Until we learn how to unlearn that belief by seeing where we didn't get what we wanted and got what we didn't need, we keep on seeing ourselves as unworthy. Until we dive into the histories that hurt us, we'll keep repeating the pattern of being in relationships that hurt. When the lessons in the patterns begin to get more bold and louder, they become harder to ignore.

Lack or abundance

Throughout my formative years and beyond, no one around me ever seemed truly happy. I began my inner-healing adventure by exploring the nit-picking and appreciation-lacking culture I was born into. I observed how the people around me were either living in the past or preparing for future events. I got clear on my lack of presence, always ruminating about my history or getting ahead of myself thinking too far in advance. I began to notice how rarely people lived in the moment, including myself.

Witnessing the lack mentality while living it created a space to see it clearly. I felt less than, inadequate, and always rushed. There was a generalized dissatisfaction, a pressing impulse to compare myself to others and a sensation of not being or doing enough. Through observation, I realized that this compulsion did not originate with me. It didn't originate from my parents or theirs either. It has been a mindset and set of beliefs passed down through generations of time, adding some traumatic events in each one that only accumulated more fear consciousness.

Lack seems to be associated with finances, but it's much more than that. Affluent people suffer from a lack mindset, being that many adhere to the pressure to conform, or else they do not belong among their peers. No matter where we originated on the spectrum of hierarchical societies, needs were denied, feelings were invalidated, and opinions were resisted. Perfectionism was a standard and expectation, and failure was frequent to many. Civility can be a form of repression, familial and societal shame, a tool for control. "Bad" emotions have become a hindrance and even considered savage; like anger, rage, disappointment, and sadness. "Good" feelings like joy, elation, happiness, and excitement are celebrated and immensely encouraged while "negative" feelings are disallowed and feared. This is emotional reality in the lack-awareness, a scary life of not enough-ness.

I felt a big turnaround when I stopped judging my pain as "bad" and actually welcomed the discomfort and exhaustion. Ultimately, I found that the pain wasn't as annoying when I allowed it and let it in. The anticipation and resistance to my pain were worse than the pain itself. The most painful place to live was in the lack of acceptance of it, the anger of it, the powerlessness of it—hence, numbing out was the most convenient go-to for me. Distractions abounded, and I kept seeking them out. I lived in resistance until COVID took me down (along with the rest of the world). Locked in with ourselves, I learned much about acceptance and abundance by feeling my own self-rejection and scarcity mentality.

There is a deep relationship between an abundant mindset that correlates with acceptance and a scarcity mindset that's associated with denial. The polarities of love and fear, presence and protection are at their core. Escaping our inner worlds with denial and numbing our feelings means denying our emotional reality. That repression only attempts to bypass what is true and natural for us. We lean away from the present moment by bypassing what is real internally, cowering in fear. We live in fear by pretending our intuitive emotional responses to life aren't important, then all of life denies us of what we truly want, and instead gives us everything unwanted. This is what living in scarcity means. It's a self-fulfilling prophecy prophesy of the most damaging kind.

Accepting each thought and feeling that comes up in our present moments is the ticket to living in the here and now, otherwise known as the only place where abundance exists. No one else needs to know or validate your experience for you to live in the abundant present moment. That's what is so amazing about it. The hard part is getting over the resistance to our feelings, exactly how we were not taught! Allowing dense feelings to come up, WITHOUT CONDEMNATION is the trick of humble observation. Compassion is the antidote to condemnation from the inside out. None of the judgment was ours to begin with anyway. It was passed down from our parents, our relations, and our ancestors. We came here to release it. Not everyone, of course. This work of releasing is only for the folks up to the task, those who can't live life any other way.

Non-judgement is essential to the abundant way of being. Abundance has nothing to do with typical "success" metrics like status, prestige, likes, and money in the bank. Abundance is an outlook, an intimate way of relating to everything in our world. The shift from a mindset orientation of lack to abundance is a very gradual, rich, experiential journey where every moment is an invitation to either at any given time in our lives. Slowing our pace reveals the choice between the two. Moving too fast takes us right where we don't want to be.

A method into abundance

The path from lack to abundance seems to go like this, from my own experience; the first choice is to note how we have options on what to do with our feelings and beliefs. Second, we decide we prefer our true feelings and opinions over their repression. Third, we cultivate curiosity and understanding that every problematic situation (what to do with the feelings and beliefs) has *at least* one solution. Fourth, recognizing that we desire solutions for managing our feelings and beliefs instead of wallowing in the problem is a disruption in the old routine. The latter is where we would linger when we live in a victim/lacking mindset. This choice leads to revealing desired outcomes. Fifth and finally, we take action on one solution to resolve said reality of feelings and beliefs. The process of shifting our mindset from lack to abundance only requires practice, as to start any new habit.

The dreaded "it is what it is" saying always stupefied me. I wasn't one of those types to blindly accept what was. I was the opposite. Rarely, could I accept anything as it was! Hence, my learning the importance of acceptance. Appreciation of what is and was shifted EVERYTHING. Acceptance would flood into my reality at an overwhelming rate. No easy lesson, acceptance comes when we release the idea of the way things "ought" to be. Putting it into practice didn't happen in solitude, though. Instead, the method calls on life's circumstances to embody the teaching.

The practical application of acceptance comes with the beautiful price tag of boundaries. Boundaries define what is yours and what is not yours. Working acceptance into life fine tunes where we end, and where others begin. Many people, can relate to how confusing this can be when they were raised without acceptance or boundaries as part of their conditioning. Accepting others' denial and others' perspectives and feelings is the ticket to abundance, respecting self and others.

Not fitting in to belong better

It took me years to find abundance in my relationships. Trying to find "my tribe" was tied into a shit ton of pain while my daughter was still learning to walk. I had a bizarre penchant for rejection. It was all shadow, a metaphysical phenomenon at play, pushing away the closeness of friendship while keeping my feelings as far from my inner being as possible. I was angry and frustrated all of the time, and I pretended I had it all together. I thought it was normal to be that way as I would lose my temper at the littlest things with my sweet little child. I wanted so badly to be un-alone, but I was repelling people left and right. My desperation was revolting, and understandably so. I felt bad that I felt bad. I felt terrible for hiding from mostly everyone, especially myself. I saved my tears for my therapy appointments; I was too angry and frustrated to cry alone. Life is hard being committed to avoidance, denial, and numbing out.

The magic was becoming aware of this pain and shame spiral. Accepting myself there, I saw and felt the rejection projection begin to grow from it. Acceptance is all-encompassing, not the opposite of denial, just as abundance isn't actually the opposite of scarcity. Acceptance and abundance *include witnessing* the scarcity mindset of denial with understanding and empathy. Acceptance *allows* for lack of awareness with a more significant all-encompassing viewpoint, expanding from it and towards the abundance of being present with whatever is. Further, allowance is a word with a double meaning; it allows, as in gives permission, and also gives energy (currency), such as getting an allowance and rewarding behavior. When we allow ourselves to accept the here and now and what is contained in it, others are invited to do the same. We give allowance to each other, a willingness to be abundantly present. This is a generous place to live, but it only lives right now. Miraculously, when we live in the present moment, we start to recognize those who are living in it with us. *Again, believing is seeing.* We also see those who refuse to live presently and are committed to protecting their scarcity mentality. Heaven on earth is built with acceptance and honesty. When people are committed to living in a lack mindset, it creates a hellish perception of conflict that is glorified as "drama."

Don't shoot the Machiavellian messenger

Months after the separation from my second husband, I would experience the most excruciating re-traumatization of my life through a romantic pursuit. I chased a fellow for many years whom I'll call Monkey Man. This guy fiddled with my feelings for fun. His approach felt like a direct and familiar projection of my stepmother's torturous superiority complex and the humiliating tactics she employed upon me. We shared one great dance that ignited a fire only his approval would satisfy. I was a sucker for the romance of that dance and quickly filled in all the blanks about who he was and what he stood for. He was clever and cunning. His humor was sarcastic and cutting, but he had a kind side to him, and I was always uncertain about which person I'd interact with. This curiosity fed me, and he kept me on my toes and in waiting. It was bizarre that I chased a man's affection. I was hypnotized by his evasiveness. He had an obscure personality, and I became addicted to winning his affection. Deluded, I believed I could get him to like me as much as I wanted him. He made me feel small and insignificant. I only wanted to be equal to someone who was convinced that I wasn't good enough for him. He needed a younger girl to marry and control. He never wanted me, but he never told me no. Monkey Man loved my attention. He saw me as crazy; I was at least as crazy as he. We kept reflecting that back to one another for years.

Never in my life did a man walk the middle path in playing with my affection. Usually, a guy likes you back, or he doesn't. Or, if he wants to use you, a man will lie to get what he wants and then leave you after he gets what he wants. He loved the distance with the promise of maybe someday. Monkey Man taught me the language of narcissism and codependency. We danced in that dysfunctional swamp until I almost drowned in its indulgence. I also learned about Attachment Theory in my unrequited aching for him. Our attachment wounds rubbing up against each other, bleeding our broken hearts together while at emotionally safe and far distances.

My debilitating codependency was glaringly obvious two years in, I received the excruciatingly loud message from this very dysfunctional and artistically deranged dynamic. Astrologer, Chani Nicolas nailed it when she said: "You can cut people out of your life all day if you like, but unless you do the deeper work of understanding the dynamic between you both, the same lesson in a different situation will repeatedly appear."

Roger that.

Life keeps teaching you the same lesson. Only it gets louder and louder until you finally learn the lesson, or else it becomes your undoing. Pema Chodron said, "Nothing ever goes away until it teaches you what you need to know." I needed to know I had big attachment traumas, and they were screaming to be acknowledged and healed. I had never been addicted to a person in my adult life before. I was obsessed with his approval like I was with my stepmother's approval when I was ten years old. Like her, Monkey Man randomly threw me a bone of consideration every now and then. Like a lab rat would respond when given a hit of sugar at odd intervals, I became entranced with the next dose of sweetness, taking the salty as I impatiently waited. As humiliating as it was, he seemed to master the art of manipulation, and I was at his disposal and mercy as I clung to my self-respect by a thread. I didn't want a mere hedonistic fling; I wanted his heart. It was a tall order for pathetic little me to want a heart so immaculately protected behind a stone wall.

The desire for adult romantic acceptance from someone least available to provide it mirrored the same ache for approval I experienced in childhood. While our bizarre "situationship" unfolded, I could translate the metaphor and symbolism of what he represented, teaching me the exact lessons I needed to learn. I became a humble student of my life and I even thanked him for the lessons he bestowed me from time to time. I was ready as ever, and I wasn't resisting my feelings this time.

At the end of that odd gift of uncomfortable circumstance, I had nothing but gratitude for the messenger Machiavellian Monkey Man. He changed my life. Rather, I changed my life when I finally said no to the monkey business and moved on. I understood him to be a mere projection I called in to teach me to take radical responsibility for my reality. He helped me see how inferior I believed myself to be, giving me the contrast to become empowered and inherently valuable. Taking responsibility for one's projections might sound elusive; it's merely an exercise in inner-observation and defining of boundaries. Through this profoundly and emotionally painful process, I gained the recognition of boundaries. Better late than never. I wish Mr. Monkey Man well. I wish every person who I ever felt resentment nothing but wellness. It would be grand if they forgave me for my insanity, as I now wholly forgive theirs.

After that experience, I learned to stay in my own lane. I also don't waste time on people who can't appreciate my value. There's no one to fix or change but myself. All I do now is share my truth with people who want to listen. Contrast teaches daily still, and for that, I am forever thankful.

I think it fitting to close with the Serenity Prayer from the 12 Step Program, Alcoholics Anonymous:

God, grant me the serenity to accept the things I cannot change,

Courage to change the things I can,

And the wisdom to know the difference.

Amen.

Stillness in Action

Write about the first responses that come to your mind with these prompts. Let the first thoughts come into your awareness without second-guessing them.

- ✓ What repeating patterns do you notice in your life through relationships? Are the patterns in your life working in your favor, against you, or both in different ways?

- ✓ Where do you feel you have no power to change circumstances in your life? Do you think it's possible to shift those thoughts so you believe you have a choice to accept events or create a strategy for change?

- ✓ What areas of your life create the most turmoil for you?

- ✓ How is the communication (self and others) around the struggle?

- ✓ What would you prefer instead of this struggle?

- ✓ How much do you prefer a different circumstance?

- ✓ What solutions are inconvenient for your current situation and why?

- ✓ Do you believe your (perceived) limitations will prevent you from finding a workable solution?

- ✓ Are you in a state of disbelief, not being able to find a solution?

- ✓ What are the reasons that keep you in your undesired circumstance?

✓ How do those reasons perpetuate your suffering and give you an excuse to keep things as they are?

✓ List your fears about making the change(s) you've not been able to complete.

Action in Stillness

✓ Assess your responsibilities. Which ones would you like to trade in for new ones? Which ones are you glad to keep?

Action Initiative

Breathwork is a great practice to slow us down, and who doesn't want to feel less hurried and stressed? Try this breathwork practice for seven days in a row to shift yourself into an abundance mindset. First thing in the morning and/or at the end of every evening (set your reminders!):

✓ Breathe in through the nose while thinking or stating "Abundance."

✓ Breathe out through the mouth while thinking or stating, "Lack."

✓ Repeat the practice for at least seven cycles per session.

✓ Notice during and after those days if you have a different awareness than before.

"It is not the critic who counts; not the man who points out how the strong man stumbles, or where the doer of deeds could have done them better. The credit belongs to the man who is actually in the arena, whose face is marred by dust and sweat and blood; who strives valiantly; who errs, who comes short again and again, because there is no effort without error and shortcoming; but who does actually strive to do the deeds; who knows great enthusiasms, the great devotions; who spends himself in a worthy cause; who at the best knows in the end the triumph of high achievement, and who at the worst, if he fails, at least fails while daring greatly, so that his place shall never be with those cold and timid souls who neither know victory nor defeat."

- Theodore Roosevelt, April 23, 1910

Chapter 7

Pause Then Play

Bottoming out

When you've hit your all-time relationship low and realize you're stuck in some kind of holding pattern, how does one conceive of wriggling out of it? I was wading in the quicksand of a frustrated existence. That was what the end of the second decade of the millennium was like to me. The thought never occurred to me to ask for a rope to get me out of the sophisticated conundrum I was in. I repelled people, I also pushed people away. Nobody seemed to be around and I was too prideful to admit I was suffering as I was. On my own private island, drowning in quicksand, as I always have been, only my symptoms were getting worse. My nutrition and chronic stress baffled me with my limited knowledge of it. My fatigue seemed to be only from working so hard physically, motherhood, and "normal" stressors life provides. Hair dye and some buzzers seemed to give me something to focus on to distract myself from the gravitational pull of my going-under.

Mid-life militancy to meek

2018 beckoned the epic mid-life crisis. Marked by chopping my curls off similar to Pink circa 1999, I rocked a butch-cut. It would be my last-ditch effort to emulate a strong and tough woman. In all of its various bold color jobs, that hair demonstrated my attempts at being authentic in my self-expression. While I looked tough with my RBF (resting bitch face), anyone who challenged the armor found a weak and yielding subservient blob of boundarylessness underneath. I was learning boundaries, and they were slippery to me during my mid-life identity crisis. Conceptually, having boundaries was beyond useful, but I lacked the presence of mind to master them. I waffled between fierce bravado and whimpering savant. It was the messiest of learning curves zig-zagging between the two extremes on a very regular basis. I was externally transfixed, until I trained myself to become internally focused. Once I no longer fixated on what other people thought, I got honest with everyone, especially myself.

The sign

With my crazy hair, I ached to be more than who I was and wore a shabby coat of inadequacy. There were delusions in believing I could achieve success, but no forward motion other than what color to dye my hair next and running my small massage practice. I lacked commitment to teaching my classes because I had an existential dilemma with the idea of destiny, maybe even a codependent relationship with it. I endlessly ruminated about the Universe really needing my work, instead simply focusing on sharing it without concern of the cosmic demand for it. I wanted banners of signs that told me the world called for my work. *I didn't understand that the world is largely indifferent to our purpose and that fulfilling one's purpose is very much an inside job.* It'd take me a few more years to realize that the Universe did not dictate my value. Instead, I'd have to figure out that I determined my worth and what I shared with the world. There would be no sign from the universe, there would be only trusting my own drive to share what I knew worked for me and the feedback I got from those who benefitted from what I shared.

Sharing what I value is part of who I am, not something I sell. The pursuit of entrepreneurship also presented its philosophical conflicts; how it's become fashionable to snub our noses at being "mediocre" as if being traditionally employed is some peasant status. The entrepreneurial industry is a cash cow. And all our dreams and delusions of grandeur may stem from a deep sense that we are not enough as we are. I admire the people who allow themselves to be satisfied with their unpretentious life without needing constant growth and incessantly striving for more.

A cog in a wheel of the world

Don't get me wrong, dreams and pursuit of purpose are great, but so is being a normal, average person who works a typical job and does nothing spectacular or unique. We need sanitation workers and people who fix broken computers. We need skilled craftsmen and plumbers. Where would we be without receptionists, landscape workers, retail and waitstaff, and local chefs? The glorification of status and recognition frustrates any well-meaning person who wants to serve while not getting caught up in the trap of notoriety. I didn't want to pursue my purpose for fame, but I won't lie, part of me ached for validation. Putting my work down and picking it back up a few times revealed the exact reason why I needed to share what I've learned. My purpose is to express and share who and how I've become for myself and anyone else that may benefit from the knowledge for themselves.

I don't want my work to be another trend on Instagram. I desire a pure kind of immortality. My legacy is to simply be the human I was meant to be, while helping others sync with their intuition and learn to love themselves as they are. My mission is to give more comfort and compassion to people who live in hyper-criticism of themselves. Leading people by my own example into their own self-acceptance is a plus; I am a success just as I am. There's the shift. That shift required a pause first.

Flipping the script to remain inwardly focused required me to stop reading the outwardly-oriented script I have been reading from. There was a process to claiming my power of defining my own success, without the measure of popularity and credentials. Revealing how alignment of one's inner-world, not the longing to fulfill the needs of others, will guide us to personal satisfaction. Embracing the inevitable suffering of daily life and framing it to serve growth also creates deep satisfaction and meaning to life. Alignment requires stopping to pause. There are no transitions, shifts, or understandings without stopping and getting a lay of the land in order to know success as a state of being.

What's at stake: feeling enslaved by our feelings, accumulating resentments, and numbing out to bear with our pain and emotional discomfort. To be fully alive is to feel and witness all the nasties as neat little messengers instead of fleeing in denial and fear when they invariably show up. *Leaning into our emotions is the way to freedom.* Not letting them control us, but by having an awareness of them and using them as tools to make necessary adjustments to feel harmony in our day-to-day lives.

We are all born into a boundary-less culture (unless you weren't, which is the exception to the rule), ruled by others' opinions and perceptions of us. Giving ourselves the right to have emotional boundaries and assert our feelings and opinions might be the biggest differentiation between a lack mindset and an abundant one. The power lies in our awareness of and respect for our emotional states which we can only do with mindful observation. Being revved up only spins the wheels.

Wisdom comes from the practice of understanding your pain and identifying your innate preferences. Escaping pain keeps us anchored in senselessness, literally numbing out psychologically. Pain is an inescapable aspect of the human condition. *Utilizing pain* is at the core of freedom. No pain, no life. I'm sorry if it was sold to you some other way. Pain is not sad or tragic. It's a gift of contrast and utility. How we decide to contribute to society in a world of distractions and endless options, we need only look into our own pain to give us the answers.

To yoke

Applying our unique individual pain to actually serve our practical lives is humbling and paradoxically empowering. The honesty of acknowledgement turns pain into fuel. Every weapon is a tool, if you understand how to use it correctly. Emotions are no different. People impulsively assume discomfort and pain are bad while comfort and pleasure are good. But the paradox belief also applies, that pleasure can be bad and guilt and suffering sometimes serve good purposes, so there are no absolutes when it comes to our perceptions of good/bad and pleasure/pain. *What our ego thinks is good for us is often not beneficial in the long run, while what feels uncomfortable generally pays off in the long run.* The irony of life is pretty amazing when we zoom out beyond the smallness of our ego. The wisdom of yoga is so popular because it harmonizes these polarities within the body and mind.

I tried plenty of yoga classes in my life and usually enjoyed the experience but often felt a lot of pain afterward. Some positions made my back worse, and it seemed every other class had some hidden position I'd regret doing the next few days after. Like any given service, yoga and all exercise instructors come with their own biases and subjective orientations. As diverse as the people in their classes, everybody is different and has different variations and limitations of movement. In yoga's essence, its purpose is to connect. The literal meaning of the word yoga means to join—and the intent is to enlighten people by practicing physical postures while focusing on breathwork to lead the way.

Since I could walk, I've been a dancer. I've taken many dance classes, and stretching was always a part of the lesson, so yoga came naturally to me, although I hated the random severe pain I'd suffer from taking yoga classes sporadically throughout my adult life. I always felt something misaligned with fully taking yoga into my life. Something about it wasn't working for me. When I thought to create a low-impact exercise class with a lot of gentle stretching in it minus the mystery of yogic exoticism, I had a strong premonition I'd not be the only one who gravitated to another way to move energy and feel completely relaxed at the closing of the session.

The IMI method's intent is also to connect a person to the inner wisdom of their instinctual nature in harmony with the physical body. It's a different means to the same end goal; growth and self-acceptance. The approach is completely different, but at the core, it is to reconnect the soul to the human body and strengthen our connection to the most valuable guidance there is—our intuition (our gut instinct), which I believe is the connection point to divinity. That may be why people have made the peculiar assumption that I am yoga instructor! Goes to show you how similar in intent IMI is with yogic principles. IMI leads to a practical union with spirit. Mindful embodiment connects the body to the heart. When people randomly ask me if I am a yoga instructor as I'm strolling down a supermarket aisle or in the middle of pumping my gasoline. I wonder, "Do I look like a yoga instructor, or do I FEEL like one?" I am sure it's the latter of the two. Maybe it's the stretchy pants. Or the knowing grin usually defaulted on my face. For sure, they are sensing my energy. Most don't realize it's their senses and their intuitive powers at play. The rare few who are well connected to their gut instincts usually just give me a mindful simile right back, which is always a moment I relish.

Like yoga teachers, I demonstrate how people can connect to their bodies through movement. The method is fun, profound, simple, personal, and also social. What I love about it most is that it helps to enhance awareness of one's physical, mental, and emotional boundaries and strengthens all of them. Yoga can also do such things. My method is deliberate and mindful like yoga, but it is not from ancient India. It came from my heart, experience, and appreciation of free-flowing, playful movement. There are no exotic names and poses, and its simplicity makes it approachable and welcoming to those who have tried everything else but failed time and time again. It's too simple to fail. I say this repeatedly in my classes, "You can't do it wrong."

Posture equals alignment

The body awareness education foundation of the IMI experience is posture recognition. In theory, slight tweaking of body part location in relation to gravity is similar to the alignment teachings of yoga. Less spiritually based and more secular, the concepts of spinal alignment are from a chiropractic perspective, physiologically supporting the healthy functioning of the nervous system. It gently tones and frees up the neural pathways and muscular messaging to lessen energetic and neural impingements, muscular imbalances, and chronic pain. Broadening the space of brain messages and body impulses, the outcome is boosted confidence and enhanced physical, emotional, and mental awareness. This fun-spirited, low-impact exercise raises endorphins and serotonin and improves circulation with playful movement. It provides a nice wave of feel-good hormones that charge up self-esteem and positive self-regard, as well as trust-building socialization.

Developing better posture habits which fell out of fashion at the turn of the 20th century, elevates a self-assured feeling. Having good posture is an art known only to those who value it, like political leaders, actors, and others in positions that necessitate it. This primary presence indicator happened to disappear from the mainstream in the 19th century. Here's another astounding facet missing from today's scene: an understanding of how the body functions as a whole! While Western medicine parts us out, only addressing one "part" at a time, the IMI Method brings body awareness back into focus, making inner awareness the guide to alignment in both the literal and figurative senses.

Mind over matter

Exercise is exercise, is exercise. Even people who stick with low-impact will feel the health benefits. High-impact is not for everyone, in fact, nothing is for everyone, why should traditional exercise be? It is crucial be open to the *possibility* that we CAN feel good in order to feel better. Believing that we deserve to feel good more often is a shift in and of itself. Sadly, too many people lock themselves into their pain patterns with their habitual beliefs of feeling bad about their bodies and themselves. IMI, being play-oriented, taps into the simplicity of effortless fun to reprogram that self-defeating viewpoint. Giving ourselves permission to play, be frivolous and less serious, expanding awareness happens organically. So instead of overthinking and intellectualizing the concept of mindfulness, the IMI method plays with it. Ironically, the integration process of the method becomes a walk in the park, nothing remotely relating to the old "no pain, no gain" strategy of high-intensity workouts.

Beyond the many multi-faceted interwoven principles of IMI, it is profoundly practical, free of complications and barriers to feeling a successful progression towards better health. It cuts to the chase for exercise-phobes. IMI is a straightforward, easy head-to-toe-based routine with a silliness streak that swings into a serious mode when appropriate. Stepping into the IMI experience requires a special kind of child-like, fun-loving bravery to boldly embrace the unfamiliar. It's a safe space among a group of non-shaming people. Quite refreshing place for many, like myself.

Pieces of the wellness puzzle

Creating the class was only a step along the path and a piece of the puzzle to finding wholeness within myself. As comprehensive as the IMI classes were, there was a piece missing. Without addressing nutrition and fostering an expansive belief system, low-impact exercise was futile if they ate crappy quality food products and spoke toxic words to themselves. Don't get me wrong, mindful exercise is very beneficial, but if the nutrition and self-talk are poison, health will not improve.

Safe to say, folks who hate to exercise are not in the best of health and often live with illness and some kind of chronic mental anguish and physical or emotional pain. Personally, I never enjoyed healthy stability in my nutrition and my suffering from chronic arthritic flareups in my neck didn't seem related to anything other than my old injury. The stress of life was severely discounted as a contributing factor. Carrying the emotional drain of feeling emotionally unsupported, took its toll on my vitality heading into my forties.

Chronic pain and discomfort of any kind are enormously stressful, and the energy of stress siphons our life force. For so many like myself, we get used to the unending pain and it feels normal to us. Not conceiving that pain-relief can happen, our bodies even resist the transformation towards wellness because it threatens our sense of stability; our ego aspect can't think outside its own limitations. That's why the only way out is to go over its head by getting out of ours.

Intuition is our instinctive nature to get out of our minds (pun intended). The path to that gut instinct is always there, however buried in busyness and other priorities. Are we able to listen to it, or are we "too busy" putting our focus elsewhere? *Getting out of our heads and into our bodies slows down our pace so we can hear the soft quiet voice of the gut.* But the insatiable, demanding ego is loud! It yells while the intuition whispers. In my experience, addictive processes and substances turn up the volume of the ego. Removing them creates enough quiet to hear our higher conscious thoughts and respond in kind. Removal of said addictions is, of course, easier said than done. At its root, requires a mindset shift, a commitment to do something different.

Trust the gut that leaks

Armed with the new tool of practicing body-awareness more consistently, the space between my pain and my digestive issues shrank. Honing into the signs and symptoms of my indigestion seemed more pronounced. The food-sensitivity tests confirmed I had inflammatory reactions to a ton of foods I ate regularly. The war in my gut microbiome reflected the battle for my overall health. Having more hope, armed with more evidence, it was all starting to add up. My emotional health was suffering from my biological health, directly caused by my nutritional choices. Go figure. Begs the question, why did this take so long to piece together?

Layers upon layers of nutritional misinformation and outdated beliefs had something to do with my ongoing confusion. Add to that, the distractions of my so-called needs and day-to-day desires like what to buy on Amazon or whether or not to like or love a post on Facebook. Navigating a reality so riddled with competing attractions makes for confusing and misdirected priorities! So many diversions, such little time. My ADHD well-scattered focus was fueled by poor nutrition. Funny how that is.

My own patterns with making unhealthy food choices had to be changed, and I saw how they had a lot to do with self-neglect, poor internal boundaries, and the absence of a planned strategy of common-sense ancestral nutrition. I marginalized what I needed, sacrificing my needs for health in the name of temptation, especially when I was around others, continually bypassing what was best for me. An expert in self-betrayal, proving to myself over and over my word had zero credibility. Broken promises keeping my addiction active, my addiction to disappointing myself. Finding the right support was a whole new adventure to take a bit longer to locate. Tired, but hopeful, answers were coming, step by step.

The steps

Support I found. Joining a twelve-step program for a sugar addiction helped me feel the support I never had. It was the start of a new life once I let others into my life and get the help I was unaware I needed until my mid-forties. Letting go of the sugar and processed carbohydrate snack foods marked the fundamental freedom to walk my talk about health and wellness. It was the holy grail, and I finally found it. Off to work on the twelve steps I went. Progress, not perfection, they say. It's not like flipping a switch and it's all up and running smoothly. Nope, recovery is a long and winding path. The only way there is one step at a time, one day at a time.

There was a lot of apprehension, confusion, and bargaining with my food addiction. Little did I know the food was creating brain fog and making my stress hormone imbalances worse. When my bloodwork revealed that I had adrenal fatigue and a hypoactive thyroid, I got serious about my dedication to my wellness, committing to daily stress reduction, quality nutrition, regular low-impact exercise, and good rest.

After a while, you get sick of hitting rock bottom. You get sicker the longer you stay there.

Is that all there is?

Those days of high stress and lack of clarity were siphoning my professional umph. I was worn down and out, but still growing massively inside my skin, learning so much about the unhealthy nuances of my lifestyle and mindset. Even though I had no energy to invest in developing my movement classes at the time, focusing on my personal growth an integral part of the development process.

I taught the IMI method at a nearby drug and alcohol rehabilitation program. The power of the class was incredible, and my heart healed every time I worked with the women's group. Teaching my method in that forum revealed how important this work was to me. Through that first time working with specialized groups, I learned to get comfortable with my leadership and not be so intimidated by it.

My relationship with marketing was avoidant, I just averted it altogether due to the revolting concept of having to hustle and sell my method. The thought of marketing turned me off. A future full of Click Funnels and cheesy ads felt as inauthentic as a sleazy car salesman on a used car lot. In reality, all I needed to do what to share my message, nothing flashy or inflated. My own alignment beckoned; I wasn't ready to put myself out there in the marketing world. Trusting that, I followed the instinct to do the inner-work, knowing that someday I'd be ready to advocate my work to exactly the right people who would benefit from it. Selling my method to a broad audience would never be my thing.

I was the exemplary poster child for "those who hate to exercise." All the blocks that came up postponed forward motion of sharing it. Locked in our houses during the onset of COVID hitting the country was the opportune time to offer my classes on social media. There was a lot of interest, but I had technical glitches and let them halt my progress. I didn't know who to ask for help and felt stuck. Spinning my wheels with a severe lack of confidence and zero vitality, my classes went nowhere when they "could have" taken off. There was a reason for everything in hindsight. I struggled in confusion as my inner growth exponentiated in the thick of it. It just wasn't time.

From fast-forward to neutral

Switching gears during COVID, I went from auto drive to neutral in one single solitary day on March 17th, 2020. I was beyond fried from my full massage practice and was ready for a break. After a few months of being homebound, I knew it was time to move forward and leave massage behind, focusing entirely on presenting posture alignment, nutrition, and general wellness strategies in a workshop format for the corporate arena. I'd advocate bi-partisan nutrition; focusing on an anti-inflammatory way of eating. The hot topic (pun intended) of inflammation and its relationship to stress needed more attention than I was giving it. And, at that time, I began to figure out how inflammation was overwhelming my stressed-out body and the root cause of my hormone imbalance and energetic stagnancy.

Pre-COVID, I spoke at libraries and small businesses about the health connection between physical alignment, vitality, and self-esteem. I attempted to move forward with debilitating exhaustion, feeling like I had weights around my ankles most of my waking hours.

My nagging food addiction kept creeping back in, I tried so hard to cut out the bad stuff but kept on caving when I came up with compelling excuses like a family celebration, a romantic date with my fiancée, or anything remarkably delicious looking out and about. I quickly compromised my convictions depending on my mood. There was a war going on inside my body; pro-health versus pro-illness. Unfortunately, the pro-illness side seemed to be winning as my lethargy and damaged skin seemed to be taking over. Eating and drinking the bad stuff felt out of my control, as if I was possessed by the bad foods. They were not my friends, and they ruled my cravings. Whenever they were out of my system, the cravings stopped. That is, until some "urgency" popped up, convincing me the indulgence would be ok, and then, it'd take me weeks or months to stop again.

I chalked up my heavy, dense energy as a symptom of emotional isolation, discounting how sugar was contributing to my depressing self-pity. I surrendered and stopped fighting it. My "give a damn" just broke. I allowed the total utter exhaustion and decided to go with it. I peeled off the judgment that went along with the fatigue and let it be. I submitted to my own state of dire weakness, wondering how forward momentum would miraculously begin again someday.

For the first time in my life, I called myself out on my own denial. I was honest about how I felt and finally admitted I was exhausted. Somewhat defeated and impeccably tired. No amount of caffeine helped anymore. I was barely sleeping. That strong woman I used to think I was left. Once I got past the feeling of failure and shame of being tired and weak, I dug into the wisdom and power of feminine yin energy. The power of pause overtook my life. Stillness and inaction were called into my totally burnt-out life.

Surrender was the only option I had. There was nothing else to do.

Masculine, Yang energy is all about the light and hard action. I had a good long run with it. Something unknown called me to move less and fall into the soft darkness and delicate place of Yin. I was cocooning, disintegrating the old, and metamorphosing. It wasn't long before I re-integrated as a whole new being, all by reorganizing my conscious awareness.

My first client was me

It was poetic that food would highlight my boundary issues, bringing alignment to them. Nurturance through food for me was wrought with mistreatment and neglect in my rearing. I was raised on cold cuts and KFC at my mother's but dined on delectable, high-quality, homemade meals at my father's. As I stuffed my face at my father's, I didn't know I was soothing myself using his wife's delicious dishes as my escape and denial of the emotional pain and abandonment I felt. Her tasty food made it ever so convenient to stuff my feelings of rejection and panic. At their home, I always overate to the point of excruciating discomfort. I ignored my sensations of fullness, suppressing my shamed feelings of envy, jealousy, frustration, and outrage. My sense of deprivation and inadequacy subconsciously enveloped me every time I ate there, while I had no choice but to numb it all out with self-deception via food fixation. This went on about once a week for from childhood, through adolescence, and into young adulthood. I learned to eat that way whenever I felt immense social discomfort. It's no secret that food is a great pacifier. I never considered my behavior disordered or thought anything of it. The patterns became clear throughout the COVID spike, I had a dysfunctional relationship with eating.

Old habits, they die hard. They are deeply engrained in the brain's neural pathways and the muscle memory of the body. Carl Jung, a well-known the psychologist conceptualized the shadow aspect of the unknown areas of our minds. It was a shadow brought to light as I healed my body through nutrition and emotional awareness. Denying my own feelings and sensations was a way of coping with consistent invalidation and minimization of others.

Thankfully, COVID forced my captivity, a closed ecosystem with nowhere or no way to escape. Before I could no longer ignore what was happening, my anxiety ran the kitchen—chasing my tail until I had a confrontation with my inner child right there in my kitchen. My kitchen anxiety was undeniable, and I had to acknowledge this sense of danger I felt whenever I was there. I always got uncomfortable in the kitchen for any extended period of time. I hated doing dishes. Dish duty was my "station" at my father's place after all our dinners. Now, instead of complying with the impulse to escape it by making a fast meal or grabbing a quick snack and leaving ASAP, I got the impulse to be with my feelings and observe them instead of suppressing and condemning them. I witnessed my fearful panic with compassion and curiosity. I was there for my shadowy feelings in the kitchen for the first time in my life. I remained present for that anxious little kid—finally! Grownup LisaBeth took the time to show up and hold space for that minimized, devalued little girl, accepting and understand her pain. Locked in my small two-bedroom apartment, I revealed all those repressed feelings. A peculiar comfort it was to acknowledge my emotional pain minus the pity party of shame and guilt. On the other side of healing that pain, a love for cooking was birthed. Now,

I wish I had more time for being in the kitchen! It feels fun, safe, and satisfying. Since cultivating the habit of listening to my inner child, she's now free to express herself wherever we are—including in the kitchen. Instead of denying her, I acknowledge her and intuitively know how to care for her instead of silencing her with distracting substances and processes.

This was the dawn of a new beginning. Dismissing my feelings was a re-traumatization pattern; denying my feelings was the cause for all my addictions and distractions. The suppression of emotional pain was internalized; what was initially received from the outside, became lodged in the psyche and caused distress in my body, which led to the chronic discomfort and hormone imbalances.

Locked away from the world of contagion, COVID-19 was an opportunity to pause and deeply heal my core trauma wounds. I learned to stop running away from my shadow in my small apartment. The pandemic brought an awakening to so many others. Awakenings don't often happen by pleasure; they enlighten us with pain. On a conscious level, they surely are anything but voluntary.

Stillness in Action

- ✓ Truth-telling practice: Write down what dominant emotions you feel most often throughout your typical days. List your passions and preferences, identify your priorities and values. Are there any persistent ruminations from your past? What emotion relates to it, if you stayed with it instead of using distraction or judging it.

- ✓ Body reconnection practice: Place your hands on each opposite arm and rub and squeeze your arms, then place your hand on the center of your chest, and make very small circles, rotating your palm slightly. Show your body you are there for it and appreciate it for just being you. Remind yourself that you are loved exactly as you are—regardless of age, shape, size, and health condition.

- ✓ After each of these practices, be still for three minutes and notice what happens to your thoughts and physical movements. What important matters and beliefs surface that demand your focus during those three minutes?

Action in Stillness

- ✓ Reflect on what characteristics you strongly dislike in others that may be a projection of what you suppress within your own personality. Being irritated by others is a great sign of projection in many cases. What we can't stand in others is usually a reflection of what we are in denial of about ourselves. Go out for a walk or to a store with this on your mind and notice what kind of interactions you have and which emotions surface. Simply observe these dynamics at play.

Action Initiative

- ✓ Set reminders on your phone to continue doing any or all of these exercises daily for seven days, no matter what. Reflect on it at the end of the week and see what surfaced to be witnessed, restored, and healed.

8

The Guest House

This being human is a guest house.
Every morning a new arrival.
A joy, a depression, a meanness,
Some momentary awareness comes
As an unexpected visitor.
Welcome and entertain them all!
Even if they are a crowd of sorrows,
Who violently sweep your house
Empty of all its furniture,
Still, treat each guest honourably.
He may be clearing you out
For some new delight.
The dark thought, the shame, the malice.
Meet them at the door laughing and invite them in.
Be grateful for whatever comes.
Because each has been sent
As a guide from beyond.

Rumi (1207-1273)

Chapter 8

Growth Happens

"All things, when they are admitted, are made manifest by the light: for everything that is made manifest is light."
—*Ephesians 5:13*

Pain's purpose

Emotional pain's utility can only be seen once we get beyond its control. Chronic pain and stress-related illnesses became the impetus for my restorative alignment. Things get messy in the cocoon phase of disintegration before the reorganization of the goo that was the mere first phase of life.

When I stopped running from myself at the dawn of the pandemic, depression surfaced quickly. After the awareness of my kitchen anxiety, I stopped judging my lethargy and told myself that it was ok to feel tired. I worked on making peace with my chronic insomnia and anxiety by simply allowing them to be without condemnation. With many reminders and some daily practice, the block of not being ok with exhaustion lifted. There were many days of constant fatigue, headaches, and neck pain. Many. Days.

The cycle of caffeine use was not helping. My reliance on caffeine over the decades had a lot to do with my fear of gaining weight again to offset my insatiable appetite. There is no question it helped to kick my stress-responses into overdrive on the regular. And being in "fight or flight" mode makes for more inflammation in the body. So, the caffeine had to go, as sad and scary as it was, it was time. However, it took another year or so to put it into practice. Instead, the pattern of insomnia and exhaustion continued. The world mid-COVID was a scary time and the financial insecurity was unbearable. Here, I was called to accept the exhaustion and all that went with it as part of the madness of the world. It seemed to be fitting.

I got good at allowing tiredness, creating a safe space for radical acceptance and self-compassion. At other times of life, pre-COVID, I would have labeled myself a lazy bum, a sloth, and a loser for "indulging" in rest. The world seemed to support the inertia I was feeling. I'd never stopped working hard until that point. It was good to allow myself to feel as badly as I did without shaming the way I felt. There is wisdom in pain when we accept where we are instead of constantly vying to change it.

What a luxury it was to do this. I was so fortunate not to be considered an emergency worker. I got to file for unemployment since my business went down the tubes overnight. I was privileged, and I knew it. I had the space and time to work on myself, how rare is that for the everyday person? I felt thankful to be exactly where I was at such a crazy time in history. Guilt washed over me. How can I indulge in my healing while others are sick or at working among the sick at constant risk of being sick? I became curious about my sense of responsibility here. I was lucky, still, it was the hardest time of intense growth and rebirth.

Life was far from a free ride. Confusion and frustration dominated my awareness. I was comforted that all of humanity was suffering, and we all had that in common now. Culture had gotten so scary, complicated, and immensely challenging. Pretending everything was fine was no longer necessary, societally. We could all stop faking that we had it all together! COVID reality validated ownership of my circumstances *and* held me accountable for them. For the first time in my life (so many first times in this brave life), I loved myself just for being human and existing. Once actually felt self-compassionately loved, a new kind of confidence started to emerge. It was humble love that was small and private. It was a welcome change from what I believed love to be before; disapproving, critical, and controlling, so far from the real thing.

The phenomenon of COVID became the "great divide" of people, polarizing groups and schools of thought. We were either stepping full-out or into our authenticity, realizing our own personal priorities (love/abundance) or gravitating to unquestioned mimicry and panicked reactivity (fear/scarcity). In essence, there was a clear choice between living in love or fear. Cue music from The Doors, "Strange Days." I found myself caught between both awareness's. In my cocoon state away from fear and transforming to love, I could see both sides.

Heal thy heart

In all my quiet time to reflect, I began to notice a subtle block which was not mental. It was in my heart. I had a wall around me and realized I was fearful of connection. I felt safer alone and had gotten very comfortable there. Heart walls are subconscious emotional shields as a result of betrayal, abandonment, sorrow, and many other responses to mistreatment. They block the ability to move forward romantically, financially, and socially in one's life in an effort to protect against future hurt. I had emotional heart walls the size of Rhode Island. Cognizance of another block felt overwhelming as I regularly revealed more layers of my woundedness. In working with a new empathic entrepreneurial coach who challenged me to be completely honest about my feelings and opinions, my heart opened up to be able to connect with someone so intimately about past hurts. Receiving such unconditional acceptance melted some layers away and go figure, some forward motion began as I popped my wings out of the cocoon.

As I maintained my soul work, more clients showed up. As I learned to trust myself, others entrusted me with their attention and guidance. It felt good to help people feel supported and unjudged on their individual sovereign path to wellness. My hard-won self-acceptance was beginning to pay off as I radiated it energetically. When you love yourself where you're at, people *sense* it and get curious. Call it a sixth sense; people detect all emotions. The root of all emotions, positive or negative, are fear and love. Only love can acknowledge the emotion of fear, but fear has no consciousness of love. Fear is the absence of love and zero consciousness. Fear is foreign to love, it mocks it, it is suspicious of it. Fear's purpose is to protect you from harm, it is fighting for your survival. Fear knows no trust. EmBODYment allows awareness of fear, and leans into tender trust as we acknowledge the need we have for love. EmBODYment is no mystical experience, it is bearing witness to the body, as you feel your emotions; all of them.

Living in the new unchartered territory of trusting my feelings more and being there for myself instead of residing in a lonely and empty place, I was comforted by simply allowing whatever came up to be seen and felt. I witnessed myself with an objective curiosity, wondering, "What am I feeling?" and "How will I respond?" Then, I got the hang of reflecting upon whatever response to whatever feeling and collecting data from my investigation of cause and effect in my day-to-day experiences. Note the word investigation. It has the word INVEST in it. Accident? I think not! The return on INVESTment of INVESTigation is precious! Conscious reflection pays dividends on our life quality. Life is never dull or empty with heartfelt experiential investigation. Instead, fullness flows through. Through the heart, the rest of the body is revitalized.

Although bearing no real value to anyone but me, I lived in fascination of processing my emotions, feelings, and perceptions. When my struggle with food addiction was illuminated, I was adamant in believing I could overcome it on my own, just as I dealt with most of my problems without any support. I faced the paradox of projecting what I needed most for myself was what I was offering others; rational and stable nutritional support.

On the surface, I seemed healthy—well, except for that rash on my face, which told another story. What I most wanted to provide for others, I had to learn to give to myself *consistently*. Because I wanted to support others, I had to get a handle on how to receive support.

Getting on the wagon and staying there

Looking somewhat fit and energetic enough to go out and about without any noticeable difficulty other than my own generalized heaviness playing out on the inside, it wasn't apparent that my food addiction and my chronic stress-induced illness was progressing. Being home more often fueled my constant desire to snack every ninety minutes and highlighted my preferences for caffeine, sugary sweets, and processed carbohydrates. Since I first gave up refined sugar in 1999, I've come on and off it many times. Being on and off the proverbial wagon played out more like a roller-coaster throughout any given month. Whenever there was some social event that had tempting foods, or I was overwrought with a craving, I'd indulge and quickly regret it. Almost immediately, I'd suffer from brain fog, depression, and debilitating lethargy. I'd have insomnia, usually all night long, waking up with no energy and needing caffeine to function. Through my investigation of my food habits, there was a correlation between my consumption and the anxiety, depression, insomnia, and bloat I felt. Every other week there was some compelling reason to ingest what I knew wasn't agreeing with my body and I couldn't understand how to stop that pattern.

A birthday, a celebration of some positive benchmark, a national holiday, there are a lot of holidays throughout the year, you know? With promises broken time and time again, I wondered why my promises meant so little to me. I couldn't figure out why couldn't I keep promises, be proud of myself, and have rock-hard oaths between me and myself. I had a case of amnesia whenever I found myself enticed by the chance to get a hit of sugar and crunchy, salty carbs. My skill of bypassing and minimizing my health priorities became so prominent and frustration only grew. I started to grasp that I had a real problem, an bona fide addiction to these offending overly processed and highly-addictive compounds.

As I learned more about my food addiction, part of the dilemma was being sure that I had to figure it out and deal with it on my own. All I ever knew was independence. Self-reliance, I thought, was an attribute until it became my prison cell. Hyper-independence is a defense mechanism. Albeit necessary for survival, it does not give credence to thriving. To thrive, we need others, and we need help. No one wins alone. This was my next big life lesson coming around the pike.

Before I figured out that I needed to get some help with my overeating addictions and consuming sugar, caffeine, and processed carbohydrates, I beat myself up for my self-betrayal, just as I subconsciously beat myself up for not doing better or being more successful throughout my past. This brutal perfectionism became my rationale for engaging in addictive behaviors. I was used to feeling bad about myself, being disappointed, feeling let down and a failure, being minimized, and not being taken seriously. The repressed emotions caused me to internalize the invalidation I was accustomed to, perpetuating that powerless sensation. There were a zillion ways to rationalize my dysfunctional relationship with nourishing myself well. I had healed myself into a corner, and the only way to move forward was to reach out.

Locked into my home, swirling in the circles of my eating patterns, I ate more often and for all the wrong reasons. I drank tea and coffee when I needed water. I overate while I was feeling full. I ate when I knew I should sleep. I snacked as I prepped dinner, often being full before I sat down for my meal. Luckily, a few years before, I gave up eating after 8 pm because I heard it would help me sleep better, so at least I was not eating at night anymore, which I knew was the worst time to eat. My boredom, insecurity, and anxiousness were the feelings that sparked my short and sweet food-fixating stints. I had no tolerance for my hunger. When I felt a tinge of hunger, I quickly quelled it with a snack. The degree of my panic varied with my blood sugar levels. If I were eating no sugar, it'd be less overwhelming. When I was "off the wagon," my hands would shake when I felt hunger. I thought I was minimalistic, eating just to alleviate the belly rumbles. I learned that snacking was the way to keep your metabolism running high, but I learned later that the digestive system needs some time to rest. Small snacking only keeps the body busy digesting unnecessarily.

To make a big meal was a whole anxiety-producing production. My constant hunger kept me from planning. The thought of planning ahead felt out of my reach. I never knew how to do it, and I didn't know where to begin. Making time to prepare food and create meal plans simply wasn't in my skillset. The whole concept of meal planning set off the freeze stress response in me. With zero clear-headedness, there was nothing rational or civilized going on in my kitchen. Instead, I lived from hand to mouth for survival and to shut my belly up as quickly as possible, so I could focus on other things. I saw no problem with my process until I was diagnosed with an autoimmune disease, Hashimoto's thyroiditis. The damage was done and the stakes were upped in overcoming my addictions and restoring my health.

The labyrinth of nutrition

There is no "norm" of eating anymore—if there ever was. There are only theories backed by scientific data to support them, and the various schools of thought all conflict with one another. People have to find what works for them on a case-by-case basis. This is no small task, with so many having dysfunction in our relationships with food and drink. Getting tested for food sensitivities is an excellent way to explore and investigate your baseline for which foods to avoid and which ones are safe. After that baseline is known, seeing a functional medicine doctor who matches up with your interests and/or doing gut microbiome tests is a good place to start. Learning about what I need, personally, by how my body responds to particular foods and supplements dictates what I feed myself, not what any nutrition guru or YouTube doctor tells me.

No one can succeed alone on a healthy nutritional journey, particularly when the plan deviates from the norm of the Standard American Diet (SAD). In this society, the pressure to cave into fried foods, candy, and processed food products is relentless. *Support is essential.* A big lesson in humility was my powerlessness without the support of others, a big pill to swallow considering my history of needing to do life all on my own. Stabilizing my nutrition began when I admitted that my willpower was not enough. The power of Spirit gave me strength. The power of people in the same boat as me gave me hope. The humility, vulnerability, and visibility gave me focus. Prayer helped a lot too. Don't knock it 'til you try it.

By setting my healthful intentions, admitting my struggles and asking for help, I got the power to commit to embodying wellness. Such a stunning example of the paradox in how personal power works.

To my own dismay, we need each other, as much as so many like myself pretend otherwise. Before the humbling experience of confronting my food addiction, I tried to function in a vacuum. Another growth spurt of learning to need others as much as I need to be needed (that's a lot of neediness, so be it!). Full emBODYment and emPOWERment will not come in isolation. They come through the humility and trust in the spirit of humanity and our higher consciousness (or God). This kind of humble power leads us to individual and collective restoration.

The restoration process to wholeness

We are perfectly imperfect. There is nothing to fix. Wholeness comes with acceptance and appreciation, without aspiring to change anything but our perspective on the way we feel and think. Once we accept ourselves as we are, growth can happen—we must disrupt the old habits of resorting to the old, outdated coping mechanisms that kept us stuck in those old behaviors. Admission of what was, not wishing it were otherwise, restores us to health by surrendering to what was and what is now. We had good reasons to cope the way we did, and giving ourselves that kind of forgiveness for our old ways frees us to move forward and leave the patterns behind.

Growth and healing come naturally when we remove the impediments with simple honest awareness. Wholeness is a way of being. Letting our uncomfortable feelings be felt is the way to feel whole. *The way we feel becomes us; if we feel incomplete, we are, if we feel adequate, we are.*

Now, for the patterns. Those habituated muscle memory patterns. Our old habits try to convince us we can't change, but it's really a lack of awareness. Once we're aware that there was a reason for our behaviors, we can see that we were surviving our best with all we learned. People can change, but we have to be ready. If we're not ready, then there's no change. Although there comes a time when we know we will never be ready, so then, we are! That's how you know you are ready!

Other people changing is not within our control. This is what we have to accept to feel the gift of wholeness. When we release the idea that others should be how we want them to be, we can let go our imagined responsibility that they need us to change. It can be an enormous distraction from our own growth. We get so frustrated with other people not being able to change, our focus needs to stay on our personal path for change to transpire. If we focus too much on others and the world not changing to our liking, we get bitter and resentful, which deflects from our own lives and responsibility to grow into our healthiest selves.

Heaven on earth

Being human gets a bad rap when raised among the scarcity mindset—led to fear that humanity is a downward spiral, headed for destruction, and ultimate extinction. The ego feels threatened and will always loudly speak of disastrous future consequences, possessing little hope for ourselves and each other. Hell on earth is when the insecure ego runs the narrative in our minds. Heaven, on the other side, feels secure and restorative. Heaven resides within each of us, in our higher consciousness beyond the overthinking egoic mind. Some argue that Heaven on earth is delusional, tinting reality with rose colored glasses, but it is a powerful force of creation, the flip side of destruction. Belief works both ways, in both directions. Think again of the devil on one shoulder and the angel on the other. In-between, is you. Feeling both as forces within yourself is the key to integrating fear and utilizing it as the tool it was created for, instead of being its servant, which only leads to our degradation and ultimate demise. Greater consciousness is the tool of recuperation and revitalization.

Are the habits in your life serving you or are you serving your habits? Is the ego running the show or is the higher mind supporting your life and growth?

"The mind is a great servant, but a terrible master," as the author Robin Sharma put it so eloquently. The ego is not a villain, its function is to protect us from danger. Our minds are a memory filing cabinet and predicting the future is the way it attempts to keep us safe. The mind a survival tool. The heart is designed for us to flourish and thrive. The mind recollects the past and prepares for the future. The heart lives in the present moment. We need harmony between the two for wholeness.

Relying more on the ego leads to our destruction, while leaning into presence, aka the heart, guides our growth. Ultimately, we're either living or we're dying. Life is either fascinating or dull, full or empty. People who are bored with their lives, living out monotonous routine, wallow in unanswered questions they never bother to broach. Those who find the awe of life embrace transitions that are inherent in the maturation process and phases of life. Curiosity is what leads people to grow and expand awareness beyond the controlling and fearful egoic mind. Heaven is in the subtleties, the little things, bringing meaning and significance to our moments. Dismissing the subtleties is minimizing the very richness of existing. Living in the past and worrying about the future is hell.

Projection of our pain, blaming the world for it keeps us stuck in the hell of unending suffering. For example, feeling rejected and deprived by others is a projection of what we already reject and deprive inside of ourselves. Regardless of what the intent is of others, feeling rejection and deprivation are feelings inside of you. They would not be felt if they weren't already there. Of course, these feelings were a response to the circumstances and did not originate with you from the start. Ultimately, what we believe about ourselves is mirrored back to us. This is projection at work, the psychological phenomenon, intangible, but insidious, much like jealousy or resentment, it can be minimized and bypassed if we don't take the time to notice how it effects the way we think of ourselves and relate in the world. The little things are significant when living in heavenly abundance among life's detail and complexity.

The power of pause

Addictions, however blatant or subdued, socially accepted or illegal, have the same purpose; avoidance and distraction of our emotional, mental, and physical pain. It serves to react to pain by turning away from it. While seemingly small, in noticing patterns of bad habits (i.e. addictions) we are leaning into pain with objective curiosity. Getting into the habit of leaning into the observation of our bad habits, we discover the illusion of fear; our pain is often more about the anticipation of an event than the circumstance of it.

Conscious awareness, the innocent witness of observing is the first tool for moving past our painful self-defeating patterns. What we prefer can only come with the second tool, articulating the new preference.

Feeling and thinking of our thoughts without immediate reaction brings an awareness that cannot be had without taking time to reflect. The pressure to react quickly is an imposition, an urgency to quell and escape the discomfort of the "negative" emotions that surface, hastily bypassing (negating, hence the label of negativity) natural feelings. Stillness, or non-action breaks the unconscious habit of knee-jerk reactivity, outwardly or inwardly. Slowing down our responses stops escapism and also reactivity.

The defense mechanisms of avoidance, escape, and impulsivity keep us going as we are, without reflection, until some necessity to stop the pattern surfaces. People only change when they are motivated enough by reaching their limit or hitting their proverbial bottom. Stopping routines that are self-harming requires slowing down the pace. The louder the pain, the bigger the necessity. Powerlessness comes up. What we do next with that feeling leads us to the mind or to the heart, to Hell (reactivity) or to Heaven (presence), to slavery (fear) or to freedom (love).

Into the unknown

Only a maximum perceived threshold of pain can bring about its intolerance. The attitude and beliefs will direct how that pain is managed. Being victimized, we plunge into the stress response or stay present with acceptance and feel a sense of victory. Victimhood is the same old, while victoriousness is a journey into the new unknown, requiring patience, courage, and curiosity. A journey into the unknown is the definition of adventure.

Solutions only come when we admit the problem first. Denying the problem denies its solution. Denying signals is barely conscious, but it keeps us in a holding pattern of emotional distress. When we identify the space of our own denial the signals that go with it, honest awareness remains. Then, awareness of what we need and want naturally arises.

Using awareness as a key to restoration is an elusive concept of repairing and revitalizing whatever was perceived as missing or damaged. It takes courage to notice what is missing or damaged. Doing so brings witness and acceptance to the current situation, identifying what's preferred and articulating it. It takes bravery to feel what wasn't safe to feel when it occurred and allow that process to soothe the part of you who didn't want to accept things as they were. Restoration honors what was, acknowledging the lessons it brought in the richly fertile and nurturing place of understanding and self-compassion. Compassion and forgiveness go hand in hand in the wobbly process of the concept of restoring ourselves to a state of wellness. Expecting a pain-free life and judging our emotional turmoil is the denial of our frail humanity. Of course, we avoid pain and flock to pleasure; these deeply encoded impulses are necessary for survival. When avoiding pain isn't as pleasurable as it used to be, we realize that facing our feelings is the only way to move forward.

The source of dis-ease

Intangible emotional discomfort develops into physical ailments and general complaints. After all, the "issue is in the tissue." Unresolved and unprocessed pain ranges from a mild gnawing annoyance of chronic body pain to high blood pressure and often manifests as life-threatening dis-eases. Functional medicine offers a systems-based approach to finding the root causes of dis-ease while acknowledging how prolonged stress and emotional distress affect the human body. This viewpoint is not widely known due to the payoff of our lack of knowledge—namely, to the businesses and industries like big pharma and diet culture who profit from our health illiteracy and confusion. This is only the tip of the melting iceberg, but I digress.

Denial is the source of all dis-ease, period. All the sick people can call me crazy and point their fingers, saying they have zero responsibility for their illnesses and no control over their health destinies. However, those who dare to look into their health will see the relationship and parallel between the stories they tell themselves and how these stories fuel their unwellness.

Recognizing the state of my neck pain is the litmus to gauge my self-care on any given day, week, or month. For example, my chronic neck pain consistently flares up with stress, sugar, and lack of sleep. The arthritis in my neck is precisely in the area where I was blocked, energetically and emotionally (same thing)—my throat.

That's where I stifled myself to manage the chronic lack of psychological safety in my relationships. My cervical spine reflects the excessive damage done, feeling strangled by the negation of my expression. Scoliosis in my mid-back relates to my heart. My body is literally twisted from not feeling I could trust my caregivers on an emotional level. Years of frustration, anxiety, and overwhelm threw my hormonal balance off kilter. I fully realize that the liberties I am taking of such bold statements could win me titles like "unhinged" and "woo woo." People who make connections like this are frequently discredited by the powers that be so they can maintain the status quo of a very dysfunctional healthcare industry that profits from breaking subjects into parts and pieces, totally neglecting how our bodies operate as a whole integrated system. Louise Hay, a motivational author in the field of healing gives a list of spiritual causes of dis-ease in her book, *You Can Heal Your Life*. According to her book, arthritis stems from feeling unloved, acne, a lack of self-acceptance, and addiction as avoidance of self and lack of self-love. This kind of slant can crack open the limiting way we used to look at what pains us.

People with type two diabetes, a reversable condition, struggle with sugar addiction. Rather than help, the misinformation given by doctors and the mainstream media on how to manage diabetes by recommending fake sugars and snacks with substitutes make symptoms worse and more severe over time. A sugar addiction is a coping mechanism that comes from unmanaged pain. Avoidance of pain or discomfort is behind all compulsions and pleasure-seeking behavior. Solve the root cause embedded in the lifestyle, and the body begins to heal and strengthen. Gabor Maté, a physician, specializing in child development and trauma, asks, "Not why the addiction, but why the pain?"

Depression has verifiable causes. It does not mysteriously surface without at least one. Treating depression with medication alone, as if there are no other contributing aspects deeply embedded in one's belief systems, is to throw the baby out with the bathwater. It's a slippery slope to go to a therapist who does not have a positive focus and uses anti-depressants because nothing ever gets restored or processed. There are people in therapy and on psych drugs who accept their misery as a part of life for decades. Anti-depressants' warning labels include suicide as a risk because the drugs can't control the thoughts, it only attempts to moderate the emotions. Medications don't alleviate emotional repression. The unprocessed emotion lingers like a time bomb in a landmine. When people feel safe to trust, which takes nothing but time and compassion, they can express their pain and feel it into balance. Shaming, fearing, and guilting emotions while wishing they weren't there push the depression and anxiety deeper into the emotional body.

Taking a pill, if at all, is one small part of a plan to solve the root cause of any ailment. My Hashimoto's diagnosis is not the root cause of my dis-ease. It's a symptom of imbalance. Constant stress, lack of enough exercise, and poor diet wore out my liver and adrenal glands, throwing my hormones into a tizzy. Taking a pill will not fix my hormones. It only will cause dependency on the pill. I owe it to myself to explore solving the root cause by eliminating what was throwing me off balance before I resort to taking any pills that could potentially cause new and different imbalances.

In a sick society, being well seems to be unwell, which is insane to consider. Stopping the madness is akin to stopping a fast-moving train. Abraham Hicks uses this metaphor for momentum often. To get moving the other way, we need to slow the train down first, gradually to a stop, so it can begin moving in the other direction.

Easy does it. Long, slow break. Screech. Stillness. Now we can begin to move the other way.

Getting witnesses

Seeing our patterns of self-neglect, self-abuse, and imbalances in health is the first step, then getting loving validation following immediately afterward guides a gentle alignment towards healthfulness. Having help is essential to every healing journey, as is time to process in solitude. Others witnessing your experience brings your process outside of your mind. Having your process seen and reflected back to you is what makes it real.

When the patterns are so deeply engrained, we feel powerless against the pain, whatever its origin. Restoration seems too obscure and scary a concept. Where to begin? Right there. Stop. Breathe in. Then out. Keep going with that for a little while until your mind tries to stop you because it doesn't feel safe enough to stay focused on your breath.

Seeing yourself

Witness it all. As many moments as humanly possible. Share what feels need to be shared with someone you trust and feel emotionally safe with. If there isn't anyone, find them. I promise you they exist in more numbers than you know. Trusting self comes with trusting others, the same goes with acceptance. Projection at its finest.

Observe the thoughts that tells you everything is bad, and you'll never get better. Acknowledge how you feel in this moment, the good, the bad, the ugly. That's the beginning. Right here, feeling the exact space you are in. Observe the desire to figure it out, but fix nothing. Watch the judgments you have, but see beyond them. Is your energy frenetic or fatigued? Is your mind racing? How about your heart? Is there pain in your body? If yes, where is the pain located? Connect to your sensations. Are your fingertips cold? What is the taste in your mouth? What noises are happening around you? Fill your lungs with air again. Exhale and notice how the air left your lungs. What emotion went with it? Is the pain still there? Do you feel shitty, perhaps? Stupid? Confused? Curious? Notice the judgments, and watch them, don't attach to them.

Acceptance is restorative. Breathing and observing creates awareness of our feelings and thoughts. This habit of focus lets us validate ourselves both from the outside in and from the inside out. Through simple witness, we recognize and allow experience just as it is. When we are practicing acceptance, we are practicing emBODYment.

Speak to transform

Sharing how you feel with another is an alchemical process— taking those feelings from the shadows into the light. Being honest and vulnerable, learning to trust that feelings are safe to share in the presence of adequately vetted others (of the trustworthy, non-judgmental, compassionate kind) allows the next phase of growth to begin. Going out on a limb and speaking about our truest feelings, needs, and preferences is an action that recalibrates how we relate with others. Speaking is bravery amidst trepidation. This means sharing whatever is—however it comes out: boldly, timidly, with meandering preambles or blatant blurting. If we share our words with people who love us, they will allow the conversation to lead to refinement and understanding.

The word intimacy applies to any relationship that allows vulnerability to say what needs to be said without fearing detrimental repercussions. As scary as it can be, vulnerability cannot be skipped, it is necessary for real intimacy. Empty and shallow connections are pretenses that may be preferred and necessary at times, but deep bonds heal our soul. Without the close connection, one seeks to fill that void with other people and things—suppressing the primary need to be seen, heard, and understood.

Admitting we need help implies we are weak, which is frowned upon but there is actually zero shame in it. Humans are social animals; we need help with the facts of life. Pretending to be strong may quite possibly be our biggest downfall. Mustering up the bravery to ask for help is the great obstacle to achieving wellness of heart, mind, and body. When we learn to do that, we can grow past our self-imposed limitations.

Stillness in Action

Here are a few questions to help you to expand awareness of your own growth. Reflect upon and/or journal the responses.

- ✓ What could be the meaning behind your own pain?
- ✓ How much time do you spend in a lack awareness versus an abundant one?
- ✓ Where do you consider yourself victorious and where do you still feel victimized in your life?
- ✓ What kind of outreach do you need?
- ✓ What communities are you interested in joining?
- ✓ Where are your people who you can feel safe with expressing your truest interests and reflections with?

Action in Stillness

- ✓ Consider the possibility that what is unwanted merely exists to help you clarify what is desired in your life. Imagine the possibility of having what you desire and feeling the faith that it could actually happen.

Action Initiative

- ✓ Spend a few minutes each day to pause when you otherwise keep moving without stopping. Plan ahead when you might practice the power of pause and also do so spontaneously whenever the thought comes like right before a meal, or when you feel like saying something, but take a moment for yourself before acting. Place a reminder in your phone or on a sticky-note to remind you. Practice pausing more for a few days in a row and see what arises.

9

To the crazy ones.
Here's to the misfits. The rebels. The troublemakers.
Here's to the ones who see the world differently.
They're the ones who invent and imagine and create.
They're the ones who push the human race forward.
While some may see them as the crazy ones, we see genius.
Because the people who are crazy enough to believe they can
change the world are the ones who actually do.

—Rob Siltanen, Chairman and Chief Creative Officer at Siltanen &
Partners for Apple, Inc.

Chapter 9

Intuitive Movement

Spirit inside a physical presence
Not a doing, a being
Who told you not to dance?
The judges internalized
Controlling every move
Will it be ok to be you soon?
Move to truth
Bounce off the energy
Imperfectly perfect
Before the fire of life.
—Poem piece, Dance

Restoration using IMI

Tuning in to how we feel is akin to finding the map to our personal treasure trove. Moving with this self-awareness method, also creates the habit of practicing better posture. There's an inverse relationship between posture and emotion. We wear our emotions in how we hold our bodies. I've witnessed stress levels drop as chronic tension is released from people's bodies. Cultivating body-awareness taps us into our precise state of being, identifying emotions, and subconscious beliefs, tracing sensations in the body. After practicing IMI, people become adept at tuning into themselves anywhere they are. Making ourselves our reference point is especially beneficial for people like me who were trained to tune into everyone else's emotions before their own. People who lean towards codependency find the boundary skill development groundbreaking, as their feelings become the primary focus instead of other people's feelings.

Showing up to play in the IMI space to observe what comes up creates a language that didn't exist for most before. Thoughts, opinions, and sensations organically come to our consciousness in practicing the simple body-awareness techniques. Noticing a feeling that triggers a thought, a judgment (of self or another), and the sensations that result from them all surface as we move to music that perfectly fits the mood. Intentional non-judgment among the group is another liberating teaching of IMI. When jealousy and envy come up inside ourselves, the impulse to compare can be neutralized as we see our habit as less than or more than in skill or beauty in relation to others. Everyone has attractive traits, not just some chosen few. It's comforting too, that everyone has flaws and makes plenty of mistakes. Life is inevitably awkward at times and we are all fumbling our way through at some time or another. The way people move is influenced by their beliefs and the way their body is designed and maintained. We are all human together. Through the IMI practice, we tap into our fun and return to the freedom of childlike expression, comparing ourselves to no one, moving for the joy of it. This practice of being lighthearted invites us to be fully alive and in the present moment.

Practicing healthy boundaries in the restorative IMI process leads to psychological safety. IMI provides the interactive exposure opportunity to better grasp healthy relating. When embarrassment, shame, and insecurity arise, it is noticed and honored with full awareness. There is no more pretending what is—isn't. In this experiential embodiment space, we train among others to be as we are with no pretense. The mirroring piece among the group is where the alchemy occurs; having others see us expressing ourselves non-verbally and physically, we learn it's safe to be ourselves socially, not in secret, alleviating all social anxiety.

With a practice of this kind we come to a place of genuine connection, finding trust where trustworthiness exists. When we are honest with ourselves, emotions are mere energetic impulses keeping our lives in line with our values, needs, and preferences. Unfortunately, many like myself, were groomed in childhood to deny our own feelings for the sake of others' comfort levels. Dare I say that modern society indoctrinated most people to be subservient people-pleasers and forgo our own needs. Awareness recalibrates us towards inner alignment and brings it back into balance.

As much fun and frivolity to be had amidst the IMI experience, dense emotions can creep up to be processed. Uncomfortable emotions like sadness, anger, confusion, frustration, jealousy, and envy get triggered to be witnessed and expressed through movement. Simple self-witness is the most direct way to release old stored energies. Expressing these feelings through movement in the company of others is thrilling, intense, and liberating. There is a primal element to expressing these feelings non-verbally. Performances can happen, especially during group exercises, but usually, individuals are focused on their own internal experiences instead of seeking to impress or entertain. We express for our own sake. Extravagant extended showmanship, i.e., external fixating is discouraged to keep our focus on our inner-reality. Attention-seeking behavior can be re-traumatizing and violate the emotional boundaries of others in the experience. Expression to connect is encouraged in times of playfulness, it is non-verbal communication, but expression to display is not the intent of IMI.

The phenomenon of mental projection is a fascinating occurrence to witness in the IMI session and it happens as often as it does in daily life, only this space is intended to fully see what we believe and how that effects our emotional state. Notice what judgments come up. This is different from discernment, which is more about observation and utilizes boundaries without negative judgement of self or others. Whatever judgments we have or feel from others is almost always projection or a defense mechanism that might need some reflection.

The physical impact of IMI is subtle but profound. This is a low-impact exercise is best suited for people who need to keep their stress levels at minimum. Consistent relaxed, free-flowing movement boosts all the feel-good hormones while toning the muscles, nerves, and hormone balances. Body-confidence comes with moving it gently and with ease. Revitalizing our bodies can be a joy and having nothing to do with pushing or physical forcefulness.

The IMI experience supports better circulation, hormonal regulation, boosts confidence, and supports the cultivation of healthy relational boundaries. Now that there is some clarity around how the IMI method serves to balance the emotional, mental, and physical aspects of our being, I will describe the general outline of the experience and elaborate on key specific techniques.

To get even more specific details and directions on how to do the IMI method at home, you can download the free e-guide, which links to video demonstrations and my curated free playlists, at my website www.inneralignmenteducation.com.

Warm-up to body awareness

Breath awareness is the first awareness to cultivate to tune into our bodies and the present moment. As we breathe in through the nose, our arms move up and around our sides, crossing at the top, over our heads. As we breathe out through the mouth, our arms go back down along the sides of the body, crossing them as they meet in front of the pelvis. We do this to get centered and feature the breath, taking us out of our mental awareness and focusing on our present, physical existence. I named the first series of movements "Animated Breath" to emphasize exaggerating the breath and the body's movements. Animated breathwork trains the internal awareness and physical emBODYment, increasing circulation and energy flow and flooding the body with the feel-good hormones of serotonin, dopamine, and endorphin neurotransmitters.

Next, we build on body-awareness cultivation with a "hinging" technique, where we fold our body from the hip joints, moving nothing else. Hinging is another foundation for developing better posture and body mechanics. Hinging leads into a forward bend where we dangle our head and release tension in the neck and shoulders, also opening up the hamstrings. As we slowly roll back up into a vertical position, we "root up" into a rigid posture defining stance, as I describe the nuance of placement of every main part of the body from toe to head. Rooting up is a practice of harmonizing our skeletal system with gravity into proper alignment. It essentially trains us to focus internally, emotionally, and mindfully as an outgrowth of enhanced physical awareness. Simply practicing the warm-up, and rooting up techniques gives the body a charge and helps to lessen lethargy. We build on hinging later on in the experience.

Cheater's core

Before we get into the movement piece of the IMI experience, we do some simple calisthenic movements that lead to punching as we contract the core. Throwing alternating punches ahead of us strengthens core muscles and can help alleviate lower back pain. So long as you can stand up and keep your balance, any beginner can do these easy core developing exercises designed especially for the most fatigued and out-of-shape people.

Intuitive movement

Then, onto basic dance patterns to incorporate full-body movement and pick up our energy. First our simple warm up with a basic scan through the body, from head to toe, focused on moving each main area independently. The we move into a series of simple rhythmic movements starting by turning walking into swaying side to side, then to step touch, we continue playing with such steps to get our legs moving. Playing around with balance and space, we go from moving in our small personal dance bubble to expanding it all around the room. Through this process, we explore what fun it is to guide ourselves casually through the room with no pressure or effort to do it "correctly." We explore with our attitudes as we walk and do playful things like the "diva-walk"—walking with a powerful gaze and determined walk, countering the impulse to have a kind, accommodating vibe. Here, it is safe to be frisky, fierce, and serious. After walking around the room, we are invited to dance freely, but it's not necessary. The choice is yours to make to do what you feel.

Relational awareness

Relating to others in group connection is an important piece of self-awareness. As we move into a circle after our diva-walking, we unify in support of each other, taking turns in the center of the circle. Being in the "spotlight," or the center of the circle, can intimidate many who have suffered neglect as they are unfamiliar and uncomfortable with a blast of supportive attention from a group. Observing how we relate with others in group dynamic gives vital self-awareness information. Again and again, notice what comes up, observing any condemning thoughts with understanding and compassion. When in the center of the circle, it can be easy to fall into an external focus, but we are encouraged to stay inwardly focused and allow ourselves to be witnessed as we move with inward guidance. Often, people respond with avoidance or performative behavior, getting somewhat lost in the dynamic, as it can be a very triggering situation. Hold onto your self-focus, even closing your eyes to stay centered, if it feels more comfortable. Remember, triggers surface to be healed, hence the power of this spotlight exercise. We are encouraged to simply walk in, pause there, and walk out if we are too self-conscious or fearful of dancing in the center. Learning to take up space and feel safe doing so can take some practice. If there is time, we will take turns so that everyone can have at least two opportunities to shine in the center.

As the center person dances or moves, the group mirrors the movements in their own unique way or claps along, with encouraging energy, supportive smiles, and warm witnessing energy. To be validated as we are, while doing what feels natural to us is powerfully restorative in relating to others. After all that excitement, we take a few animated breaths together and go into the cool-down part of the IMI experience.

Stretching awareness

Stretching and lengthening not only release muscular tension and calms the nervous system, it also develops presence within our bodies as we feel into the positions. Nervous tension and stress leave us with every relieving sensation. There is nothing strenuous or forceful about it. We play with different types of breathwork and are encouraged to stick with whichever feels best to us individually at the moment. Lengthening the body one area at a time starts with the same scan as we began with, from head to toe. Some stretching on the floor with hinging, alignment, and gentle core strengthening are built into the cool-down process. We end the IMI experience in chairs, stretching, and practicing a seated version of the "rooting up" technique to "plant a seed" of better alignment while in a chair. This is especially useful for those who do most of their work while seated, as I did much of my office work before I was a massage therapist.

Stillness wrap up

Seated in a circle, with a candle in the center, the music is turned down low, and a "gratitude scan" begins. Another head-to-toe scan, this time with the gentle touch of our hands runs from the crown of our heads to the tips of our toes, sending appreciation for our entire body as it is today and what it just did for our body, mind, and soul. A short meditation follows right after. The stillness fosters more inner-awareness, observing how we feel after the IMI experience. We witness our thoughts, beliefs, and feelings. We notice our external awareness of others sharing the space. Are we judging or comparing? Do our thoughts evoke joy or jealousy, elation or envy, celebration or shame? Are we feeling serenity, peace, acceptance? Is there any confusion, or are you calm? Everything is safe in our witnessing. Without judgment, note the opinions, beliefs, and feelings that arise and let them be. The awareness only grows. Here, we detach from our opinions, beliefs, and emotions and intentionally do *nothing* with them. We let whatever thoughts and feelings come in and out of consciousness, cultivating simple presence and peace of mind detached from our emotions. In presence, we can feel thankful for all the perceptions and emotions that came up to be seen, heard, and felt.

IMI aftercare

As the live and virtual class closes, if there is time, we may decide to share a few words about our experience among the group, which is optional for everyone. It's a time to honor the process of our expanding awareness, share our truth and express it in words.

After leaving, it's time to INVESTigate your experience and dig deeper into whatever beliefs came up by doing some journaling or any kind of reflection with a walk or by some other creative expression in solitude. It is undoubtedly helpful to share your realizations with someone you trust after you reflect first on your own. Try not to skip the solitude step! Developing an intimate sense of self-trust is essential for healthy relationships within us and with others. Healthy relations need firm boundaries. So, we cultivate a healthy relationship with ourselves first. Inquiring into our own beliefs and where they originated leads to our understanding and self-acceptance. Prematurely sharing the experience with others can disrupt this means of restoration.

The IMI method is more than adequate for processing and growth work on its own. However, sometimes additional processing time may be required. Bypassing the processing of old beliefs and emotions only perpetuates them as they continue to cycle in our present lives into the future subconsciously. Taking our teachings from observation to understanding allows us to mature emotionally and spiritually (they are so closely tied), acknowledging the rich ecosystem of our sophisticated soul. Aftercare is not essential; it is recommended if some upsetting memories or intensely negative feelings surface, which call to be reflected upon in hindsight of the IMI experience.

Alignment practice

Awareness is the real teacher; it is the parent inside us. Awareness guides our actions to nurture and support our well-being. Like a neglectful inner parent, a lack of conscious awareness is where we all go awry when destructive and addictive tendencies intercept our best intentions. The IMI method is a foundational body-awareness practice of the science of emBODYment. The lessons are not expressed in a vacuum. Instead, they are often organically be diffused into daily living. Once seen, you can't unsee it. Conscious awareness works this way.

Especially for those who sit all day as they earn a living, it is vital to work self-care breaks into the routine (one or two five-to-ten-minute self-care "meetings" in your day works wonders). Setting a couple of reminders to "root up" a few times a day will keep the energy flowing, helps the body to feel less stiff, and keeps us centered inside our bodies all day. After some practice, sitting upright will feel more comfortable. Sitting in the "old" way will feel less comfortable, gradually and gently improving posture and overall vitality, especially regarding circulation, nerves, and stress hormonal functioning.

We begin to care more about our bodies as these exercises become habitual. We are learning to focus on ourselves, and the IMI classes teach us how to care for ourselves when our bodies message us for a reprieve.

Stillness in Action (After the IMI Group Method)

Here are a few questions to help you make the most of your IMI session—journal the responses to explore the lessons within.

- ✓ What happened that struck you or surprised you?

- ✓ Were there any judgments that you had for others? What were they?

- ✓ Did you feel there were judgments against you by others? What do you believe they were?

- ✓ What needs, preferences, feelings, and opinions surfaced through the movement practice?

- ✓ How can you honor what surfaced for you?

- ✓ What takeaways did you have from the experience?

Stillness in Action (After Exploring the IMI Method Solo)

- ✓ What happened that struck you or surprised you?

- ✓ What judgments did you have of yourself and the experience?

- ✓ What needs, preferences, feelings, and opinions surfaced through the movement practice?

- ✓ How can you honor what surfaced?

- ✓ What takeaways did you have from the experience?

Action Initiative

- ✓ Experience the IMI Method privately (in its entirety or just sections of it) every other day for a total of seven times and then reflect on any shift in awareness of your body, mind, and emotions.

✓ Try a virtual class free. Go to my website to sign up!

10

"*Our deepest fear is not that we are inadequate. Our deepest fear is that we are powerful beyond measure. It is our light, not our darkness which most frightens us.*"

- Marianne Williamson

Chapter 10

Rewiring & Reprogramming

"We surrender to win, we give away to keep, we suffer to get well, and we die to live."

—John P, AA, *Big Book 2nd Edition*

Hardware and software

While soft and fleshy, our bodies are advanced organic technology. They are miraculous, so long as nothing impedes their development. Through them, we learn, creating systems of action on all levels of consciousness, voluntarily and involuntarily. As adults, we run the same programs coded in us as when we were young. The only way to change the programs is to write-in new code. Gradually, over time, new codes replace the old ones. As similar as we seem to computers, our hardware also upgrades as a response to the software updates. There is never a sudden switch-over from one program to the next, it is a gradual process of replacing bits of data with new data as new information (a new perspective) is processed.

Like creating new paths on a hiking trail, venturing onto a path that wasn't seen before demands vision. Also, traveling into unchartered territory requires more energy at first. After enough time walking along a new trail, traveling it becomes effortless because the mind recognizes the familiarity. The mind feels safe with familiarity, which is why newness is so very uncomfortable. Old unused paths get overgrown and fade into the scenery. In our nervous system, old habits of thought and behavior atrophy and vanish by etching new neural pathways and muscle memory. This isn't done overnight, as we may have heard how long it takes to create a new habit. Some say twenty-one days, and some say it takes ninety days or even twice that. Neuroplasticity, also known as neural plasticity, or brain plasticity, is the ability of neural networks in the brain to change through growth and reorganization. Pascual-Leone, a Spanish-American Professor of Neurology at Harvard Medical School, defines plasticity of the brain in the Annual Review of Neuroscience in 2005:

> "Plasticity represents an intrinsic property of the nervous system retained throughout life that enables modification of function and structure in response to environmental demands via the strengthening, weakening, pruning, or adding of synaptic connections and by promoting neurogenesis. This means that the brain does not remain static but, instead, continues to change as the obligatory

consequence of each sensory input, motor act, association, reward signal, action plan, and awareness."[10]

Glitches in the system

Creating new neural pathways enable us to update our lives. Identifying our barriers to these updates requires objective observation. These barriers or "triggers" keep the old program running, which lies in our Sympathetic Nervous System's (SNS) emergency and stress response. Getting "triggered" happens in the SNS. Reacting to triggers from the environment or from own thoughts is a fight or flight "software" function protecting us from conscious or unconscious threats. Triggers are anything that significantly affects your emotional state, causing extreme overwhelm or distress. The challenge is to become conscious of our triggers and remain in observation-mode as we investigate the experience them. We keep activating our old triggers until our awareness acknowledges the trigger and calls it out as outdated code! Remaining calm enough to witness our stressful events draws attention to the outdated, ineffective program of that particular trigger. The next step is to interpret the meaning of the trigger. Our triggers are our yellow brick road, leading us right to our old programs, so long as we don't allow them to get the best of us, acting out from anger, hopelessness, and fear with blame and projection. Otherwise, we go into autopilot once again, feeling victimized by our circumstance, possibly with guilt, remorse, and resorting to self-soothing with our old tools in the old toolkit (process and substance addictions, blame, the 5 Fs of fight, flight, freeze, fawn, and feed). They can be our gifts, our guide to self-

---

[10] https://pubmed.ncbi.nlm.nih.gov/16022601/

awareness, not anything to resent or feel shame about. Updating the code happens when we act from our calm awareness instead of reactively enacting the old habit. New habits are formed in the pause and choosing an alternate route of action.

Many of our old programs have bugs in them. These glitches feel "off" and are notifications alerting us that we need to upgrade that code (programmed belief). Thank the trigger's alerting system, for these alerts create accountability instead of blame-shifting and projecting our programs onto our perception of others. Failing to take responsibility for our programs, we miss the lesson and lose the opportunity to update them. Minimizing, suppressing, or numbing-out of our pain keeps it going, suffering the same triggers in different situations. Until we utilize the trigger as an *alerting mechanism* to upgrade our beliefs, the physical, mental and emotional symptoms of pain and discomfort inevitably worsens. The defense mechanisms and undesirable habits that run these old programs intensify, and our health is sacrificed as the final outcome, or have you not noticed?

To know power, know powerlessness

Then, the only way to harness of inner-power is to *become aware of our triggers* that cause us to (subconsciously or consciously) feel powerlessness, stress us out, and force us to react in ways that don't serve our greater goals. Perhaps you are starting to see how contrast teaches us the lessons about what we want and don't want. The trick is reframing the experience to get the new code and that is done with the power of honest observation. Self-made, successful people know how to triumph. There is no real success without some painful process. Pain averters also avoid their power.

While this is usually an unconscious phenomenon, the denial of pain subverts our inner-power. It's the crux of self-enslavement.

The topic of power is laced with triggers for most and I was no exception. Our past associations with power can block our stepping into it. Asking ourselves who we associate power within our past and what messages we received from people with power will illuminate how we feel and believe about power, assertiveness, and influence. The negative associations we have of power will obstruct our own. Power has two sides and using it for good is a wonderful gift to deliver harmony and support success at no one's expense. Most of us, including myself, got the message that those who have power abuse it, with manipulation, control, and exploitation (however subtle). Only seeing power negatively holds our natural good-intentioned power hostage. The word power must be re-programed and neutralized for anyone who has felt victimized by people with power.

We need to be accountable to our own old powerlessness program to outgrow it and claim our own inner-power. The growing pains in pregnancy and labor are great metaphors of being powerless (admitting) to the pain and delivering sheer power: no pregnancy, no labor, no birth. There are no fruits of labor, no fulfillment, without the pain of growth from weakness and into strength.

In doing what we "will," the choice is ours. Commanding power of our will by witnessing our lack of it brings alignment of our long-term desires instead of our short-term gratification. Our "will-power" can then be used for what we really prefer. The labor pains of loving ourselves this way courageously leaned into. Delaying gratification is an act of decision a.k.a. will. Living a life of instant satisfaction and indulging in quick fixes for a long time gets us nowhere near our goals. After a while, we get bored with spending time wallowing in instant gratification like social media, YouTube, and Netflix. Sometimes we need a nudge to lead us towards accomplishing bigger visions.

A higher consciousness to connect with regularly through stillness and devotion protects us from losing sight of our greater goals. Although I played in the distractions for years, my nudges were not subtle. Alignment via re-programming is a life-long process and the upgrades come just the right time. When there is a drive or curiosity, one can only spin their wheels in the mud of self-destruction for so long. Short-sightedness cries out for correction when dreams beckon loud enough.

What makes power

Power can seem elusive to learn. EmPOWERment emanates from a centered state of self-awareness. Power of authority, like governmental power, or external influence, is different from assertive inner-emancipation. Pursuing goals leads to power because thoughtful action is required to move towards them in the face of doubt and uncertainty. Pushing beyond perceived limitations builds fortitude. Boundaries, patience, and calm generates backbone. Fire (decision and action) forges strength. No mud, no lotus. No inner-vulnerability, no inner-power.

As adults, we're given the free will and decision-making power to make good use of and change our life experiences. Without understanding life as a series of teachings, we miss the whole lesson. EmPOWERment is knowing we are being schooled by life on the daily. We receive the original program in infancy, and childhood upgrades the program to version 2.0, while adolescence brings version 3.0. All other upgrades are by choice—or not.

True inner power lies in the heart and the present moment. Owning our heartbreak opens up the heart, awakening the power of our own preference. Our preferences are our power! Feeling safe in our skin is powerful, being emotionally stable is powerful, and dignity in our inherent worth is powerful.

Willpower cannot live in isolation. Actually, willpower is not achieved alone. We need others to hear our preferences and assert them—others who CAN hear us, not those who refuse to listen. I missed out on knowing power by pretending to be strong when I wasn't. Now that I admit my own weaknesses, I feel my strength. Owning my powerlessness without judgment is where I found my power. That kind of bravery is powerful. I learned to give myself grace for all the shame I felt around weakness. In forgiving my many mistakes and skewed perceptions, I could move forward and release the past with peace in my restored heart.

Power is honesty

I forgive myself for:

Living in fear most of the time.

Submitting when I knew I knew better.

Yielding when I wanted to fight.

Giving up when I knew I might win.

Allowing others' beliefs to be more important than my own.

Feeling like a failure.

Being overpowered and defeated.

Feeling convinced I wasn't as smart, and others knew better.

Sensing I was wiser, but no one could acknowledge it.

Psychological rejection and emotional abandonment.

Being conditioned to hold back and bite my tongue.

Giving up and avoiding.

Escaping via dissociation, among others, with food.

Fleeing the family, with distance.

All the isolating ways I coped.

Taking on their projections on as mine.

Rushing myself and letting others pressure me to move more quickly than I wanted to go.

Suffering for so long.

Pretending I was strong when I was in agony.

What makes trust

I unknowingly felt defeated, disappointed, and deflated throughout most of my life. My subconscious storyline was the paradox of not knowing how to trust others but allowing myself to be drained by stressing over other people's perceptions. There seemed no alternative to deal with the difficult, overpowering adult personalities I encountered as a child. I felt trapped by their authority and power. They minimized me. In turn, I minimized them as I minimized myself. As an adult, I projected the same dynamic in all my relationships. I felt trapped, I didn't trust, I froze,

I fawned, I filled, and I flew. I fought, but only when I was cornered into it. Constantly stressed out and defensive, my resentments stacked up on each other. My mind flourished with my guarded heart, intellectualizing societal dynamics and the injustices and dysfunctions that went with them. I understood the evils of the world too well. I lived it in my family of origin and lived without the ability to trust anyone—mostly myself.

Eventually, it became so uncomfortable that it could not be ignored any longer. Disempowered and codependent, my life force was siphoned by my compulsion to acquiesce and placate while not being able to feel safe with 99% of the people in my world.

In the same boat

All that neglected undercurrent of powerlessness was rooted in self-doubt. Becoming conscious of that blew me away as I used that awareness to grow self-trust and out of that my inner-power expanded along with it. I worked hard at denying my powerlessness for more than forty years. To acknowledge it was humbling and eventually liberating. Humility is emPOWERing, go figure! I learned to settle into this lesson for about a year, learning to trust my own truth; my feelings, thoughts, and beliefs. I began to feel ready to share my truth with others who could understand. The path to my liberation, to learn how to trust myself healing the shame relating to my powerlessness. Finding a community of people to express that truth gave me resilience. No longer tied to other people projecting their shame and other repressed feelings onto me. Before this, I was a dumping ground of oblivious people's projections; their fear, jealousy, anger, and all the other denied nasties they didn't want to own went directly to me. I was ignorantly giving them permission to project their negativity onto me. This is an extraordinary energetic phenomenon I now know as transference. When I joined a food-addiction group that followed the 12 & 12 (The Twelve Steps and Twelve Traditions of AA), it gave me a safe haven to learn boundaries, self-trust, and reliance on others in a healthy way.

Bravely framing my eating habits as an addiction supported stopping the pattern of sabotaging my restoration of my health. Out of sheer desperation, with nowhere to turn, I fully accepted that I could not heal my body alone. Finally, I could stop trying to figure it out without support. Joining Sugar and Carb Addicts Anonymous activated all my triggers of self-doubt and distrust. It was fascinating as I witnessed these old beliefs, knowing it was only my perception clouding my lens of the experience. When I joined the fellowship, I told myself I didn't belong, but then I knew my ego was trying to protect me from this sense of danger of being in a group. Instead of feeling shame, I felt free—what a nice change of pace to have things in common with others and share my struggles with things like "slips" and "sugar hangovers." We courageously shared our real-life struggles and emotional pain as if it was almost no big deal. So, refreshing to be in a space of psychological safety.

Projection is a pretty amazing phenomenon; what a gift to utilize it when my triggers came up in the meetings. It's all too easy to project. We're feeling uncomfortable and seeking an outlet to blame instead of reflecting. The result is usually judging others instead of noting our shortcomings, shitty sensations, and limiting beliefs. When I notice myself doing it, it's a gift so I can acknowledge, accept, or process what I'm pushing away and reflect on it until it releases. Finally, I learned to own my emotions, feelings, and limiting beliefs—better late than never. There are many slogans in the AA culture, and one of my favorites is "Principles over personalities." It means we practice honesty, humility, compassion, tolerance, and patience with everyone, whether we like them or not. Putting principles before personalities teaches us to treat everyone equally. What a great reminder to have respect for all, regardless of our personal biases, projections and judgements.

Infinite refinement

EmPOWERment is a process and very much a practice. Once you get the hang of it, it gets easier to recognize where it's lacking and how to instill it. Powerlessness will creep back up every so often, signaling we need a momentary check-in and adjustment. So long as we aren't moving in fast forward, we can notice it shortly after or even while it occurs. When I cut caffeine and processed foods out of my life, I cut the crap metaphorically and physically. Boundaries define our relationships with every person, place, and thing. No small concept, they are *the* connection to the outside world.

Taking an honest inventory and ownership of my past through the twelve-step program showed me how to solidify the process of claiming my God-given power. My old judgments were seen from a fresh angle, owning my old inaccurate perspective. Recovery from my chosen drugs of sugar, caffeine, refined carbs, fried foods, unregulated social media consumption, and book hoarding (Amazon thanks me) gave me freedom to focus on what I really want to INVEST my energy into; my life, free of the noise of avoidance and distractions. I take it "one day at a time" (another commonly spoken AA phrase), reminding me to stay present and not get ahead of myself as I used to do incessantly. Abstaining from my quick-fixes gives me power. Substances are substances, and abuse is abuse, legal or not, consciously aware or not. Anything that makes me feel remorse or like crap afterward but I keep on engaging in, is self-abuse—just like an illegal drug. Addiction seems to be encouraged in our culture via marketing and trends, perhaps my own experience, I have a strong feeling I'm not alone here.

Don't discount being addicted to our habitual thinking patterns too. I was addicted to anxiety and depression for most of my life. I felt bad that I felt bad and the vicious mental torment kept cycling, just like any other addiction. The easiest drug to see this is through the lens of my tobacco habit. I knew it overstimulated me, made me smell bad, and gave me bronchitis every few months. Yet, I kept smoking. That is until I couldn't live with my smoking self anymore.

Addiction is great preparation for finding our power. The absolute relinquishment of power in addiction helps us to claim it in recovery. EmPOWERment is innate; stripping away all the lies of our old inadequacies and unworthiness to discover an ultimate liberation in this lifetime. I believe my main purpose is to learn about love and power in this life. To indeed find love and power, I got to experience the absence of them for me to discover it myself fully.

The power lies in the momentary self-loving decisions to do what is best for ME, even if it is uncomfortable or other folks aren't happy. My preferences are as equally worthy as anyone else's. Now, when choices conflict, my own needs come first. This orientation does not make me selfish; it makes me self-respecting. It's about time for that lesson in the foundation of self-love; honor and respect.

Fail to win

Every time I "relapsed" on sugar, I had guilt-ridden remorse, and then the revelation came to me that I was comfortably familiar with feeling failure and not-enoughness. Disappointment and failure were a setpoint in my old program. When I learned to stop numbing and stuffing my feelings, I instantly felt a surge of new confidence. New momentum started running the train toward where I wanted to go instead of backward. I initiated the decision to create a new habit, to pause instead of reactively running the old code. I kept pausing before impulsively reacting and choo-choooo, up the mountain I went. The little steam engine huffed, "I think I can, I think I can, I think I can." One hill at a time.

Instead of subconsciously pushing my goals further outward into the distant time of never-never land, I started sensing success in my daily routine and more and more moments. Success is a mindset, not an accomplishment. Being a part of a community that gave me hope and support made all the difference in the world. Something transformative happens when you feel seen and heard. Mirroring is magic. The need for reflection is part of our human biological makeup, and it's pretty miraculous when we feel it working in healthy relating.

My urge to feel defeated gradually vanished as I developed presence through the emBODYment practices of IMI, stillness, breathwork, twelve step work, reflection, and devotion. Observing the root causes of my outdated limiting beliefs of feeling deprived and inadequate without the old condemnation stopped me in my tracks, allowing the train to go in the direction I preferred.

Claiming the present moment is the power that puts the past to rest. Reflecting on the past, using it as a tool for growth when we get triggered in real-time, comforts our hurt little inner kid and tucks it in with snuggly blankets. It is soothing to that child—what a relief.

No one wins alone

While we must walk the unique path to our health and healing individually, here is yet another paradox; connection with others makes it possible. "We are walking each other home," as Ram Dass put it. Success in overcoming blockages to our full effectiveness lies in the relationship to self and relationship with others.

Independence + Interdependence = Balanced Healthy Society

We need each other: not in the clingy, codependent sort of way, but as humanly designed. We are social animals and need others to thrive, like wolves need their pack. Those in antiquated religion and leaders of groupthink linger in the dogma of judgment and exclusivity—shaming people who struggle and banishing them with indirect and discreet humiliation tactics. *The Course in Miracles* teaches us that people's actions are either from love or begging for it. "Bad" behaviors are attempts to alleviate pain and vie for relief. Nowadays, more and more people find their communities by their interests, guided by their personal needs instead of clinging to traditional religion if no authentic connection exists. Thanks to social media and the smartphones, we don't even need to leave our homes to find community either. This is both a blessing and a curse. The ease of self-isolation is tempting, yet it's easier to develop ties with whom we so choose.

We need one-on-one relationships where we can be open and honest about all our lives. There is no shame in finding a support person or community to address several different aspects of our lives. Connecting with a mental health-affirming therapist, a reiki practitioner, a pastor, a skilled therapeutic bodyworker, a special-interest group, and/or just a good friend helps us to stay honest to others and ourselves.

Sugar & Carbs Addicts Anonymous (SCAA), is diverse as any religious group with different cultural backgrounds worldwide. Our differences are irrelevant. We all were in the same boat, wanting to leave sugar and refined carbs behind. I loved that we had something important in common, regardless of our backgrounds and circumstances. This community gave me the tools to meet my long-term goals. I wasn't alone in my struggles with food anymore. I had backing from people and a renewed connection to my higher power. Nutrition coaches suggests specific guidelines and customized protocols for your lifestyle, this group gives you tools to learn to stop abusing the foods that prevent health. Having a coach is helpful for specifics in establishing and maintaining healthy eating, while this group supports abstaining from "drug foods" that we hate to love. A coach can support avoiding these foods if they specialize in food-addiction, but it's still a different kind of dynamic. There is power in the group dynamic. There are many groups that use the AA program, their tools apply to any self-abusive habit, as does Recovery Dharma, a Buddhist take on addiction recovery. There are so many group communities out there, it only takes a bit of open-minded research to find the right fit. I'm a big fan of group dynamics, but I do not mean to say anyone else will benefit as I have. Every person has different needs. Listening to your inner guidance will lead you to the group that will support your goals, if groups are your preference.

Sharing and learning from the group communities incentivized my accountability. Fellows bared witness to my actions, cheering me on when I was doing well and unconditionally holding safe space when I wasn't. Honesty is a practice that is a lifesaver. Truth-telling is the bridge to confidence and sovereignty. The twelve step groups were a training ground to have more honesty in all my relationships and exposure therapy. Group dynamics were highly triggering for me, and there I could learn to feel safe among a group. I tested out my sea legs in reaching out to people, muscles that needed a lot of training. Reaching out for support to those who could provide it repaired my heart deeply. It strengthened thy willpower to do what is best for me instead of following the unhealthy cultural norms that lead to debilitating progressive diseases.

If denial is the source of all dis-ease, then honesty is the antidote to all health. No honesty, no health. No trust, no truth.

The stakes get higher

We must hit rock bottom before we rise from the ashes. Without the bottom, there is no stopping. I had to lose my health to find it. By the end of year two of COVID, I still had an odd case of localized eczema or rosacea, my neck pain was at its worst, and I was getting real hangovers from sugar and other random foods. My discomfort was complete with insomnia, lethargy, concentration issues (brain fog), nausea, migraines, and neck spasms. Cutting the caffeine, sugar and carbs helped, but my symptoms didn't entirely go away, so I knew I needed to dig deeper and find the right support.

I sought the expertise of a functional medicine doctor who specialized in the gastrointestinal tract. She dug way deeper than my primary care physician. The comprehensive tests confirmed I had leaky gut and the autoimmune condition Hashimoto's, chronic lymphocytic thyroiditis. The unrelenting stress and poor coping mechanisms throughout my life caused my immune system to malfunction and my thyroid to wear out. My adrenals were also taxed, as the two organs work together to deliver regulate metabolic hormones all through the body. The leaky gut was a symptom severe food sensitivities and intolerances, which is also not the root cause. Happy to be on the trail, I was getting some answers to my dilemmas. The culprits were high carb foods (refined flour, sugar, alcohol, legumes, nuts, and seeds). They tore apart my GI tract, literally. Once they were eliminated, my energy started to return and my mind got clear. Getting my gut into repair mode shifted my alignment into high gear.

Something about declining health that nudges one to get serious. Either that, or people give up there. A sort of line in the sand, isn't it?

Hardware upgrades

The art of getting out of your own way sounds easier than it is. As we realize we are the only thing standing in our way from being healthier, we have to reprogram the limiting beliefs that cause a cascade of undesirable consequences. These beliefs tie to the core software program that screams for an upgrade. If we don't believe we can get better, have what it takes to grow past the perceived limitations, or feel worthy and deserving of living the outcome of wellness, we won't restore our rightful health. Mindset and perception awareness comes first. Humility and honesty are close seconds. Action follows.

Feeling sluggish all the time makes it hard to move. But moving lifts the sluggishness. How can we begin if we are too tired? How do we upgrade the hardware that is our physical form? Baby stepping is my recommended method for getting moving. Forget about the gym and what you think you "should" be doing to exercise. Start exactly where you're at and go at a pace that is comfortable without any expectations of doing more. If you rarely get out of the house, walk a bit around the perimeter of each room and upstairs if you have them, for no other reason than to move your body more. Walk around the block if you feel you can comfortably without pain. Set an appointment daily or every other day, or just twice a week to do so, and commit to it. Set your own pace. Park farther away in the parking lot to walk a bit longer. Take the stairs, and take your time doing so if you can. Walking is the best movement there is by far. Our bodies are designed for it. The second-best type of movement is freestyle dance. Moving and freely shaking things up gets us embodied. Put on some pop music or whatever music you enjoy, dance awkwardly on purpose and see how that feels. Intentional awkward dancing is a fun way to embrace how silly many people feel when they dance around solo or with others. Silly-feeling dancing is a powerful way to release stored shame and guilt because releasing the pressure of needing to do it "right" is gone.

Notice what is triggered (judgments and feelings) within you when you start to walk or dance. What beliefs arise? Are they trying to stop you from continuing? Even if they are, keep going, and keep listening. The mind will chatter away if it's not used to the movement. It will try and stop you because it fears the unfamiliar. Stay with the unfamiliar. Witness all the beliefs and feelings with curious respect. Inhabiting the body is an unfamiliar experience when we live in our heads for most of our lives. Moving can take getting used to. Be patient with the process. Our hardware obviously changes with repetition, but our hormones are affected almost instantaneously. Notice what physical changes happen as you move and in hindsight. Did you sweat a little? Get your heartrate up? Did you smile? Did you frown or pout in frustration? Here we have emBODYment. We are putting concepts into practice and coming out of our heads and into our bodies. Start slowly, consistently, and changes will transpire.

Walking is the number one integrative exercise that most people can do naturally. It clears the mind, calms the body, and tones the heart. For most people, walking in the morning and at night is ideal, but walking once a day helps keep the circulation and energy flowing in the body. If you don't exercise at all, start with walking more—and more, and more. Don't overdo it, or you'll overwhelm yourself and stop. *Set small achievable incremental goals.* Going from zero to sixty will only cause more pain and halt your progress, restoration does not happen this way. It is gradual and consistent.

After the walking, if you can, take a bit of time to stretch your legs, hips, and trunk and feel the tension leaving your body. (You can check out my e-guide for safe and simple stretching tips) Observe any judgments and feelings that come up. Don't rush through lengthening the muscles and releasing all the tension in them. Cultivate presence with the process. Stretching is meditation in motion. Lessons of self-awareness come with every motion. Observe more, judge and react less. Notice how you feel after the walk and/or stretching. What came up inside your mind? Honor it all.

Paradoxical as it may seem, stillness is at the core of life upgrades. Doing nothing IS doing something, a constructive something. Stillness trains the observer inside us, and life gets richer with every session, every pause. Use a timer or not, totally up to you. Sit for three breaths and witness what happens for a few seconds. Start small and build slowly. What comes up? What limiting beliefs? Do you have time? We never have time when we feel rushed. When will there be time just to be? When we prioritize time, that's when. Stop the train and watch what happens in your mind and in your body. How do you feel afterward? What triggers came up to be seen and heard? Can you celebrate them? Yay triggers! Being honest with ourselves is the den of trust. Wellness begins with being present inside ourselves. A Buddhist saying calls us out on our hurried minds, "If you don't have time to meditate for ten minutes every day, you should meditate for an hour." Calmness is cultivated in the pause. It's a muscle that needs to be strengthened, like any other desired aspect of the body and mind. No one is born calm in today's world.

Your presence will gradually, never suddenly, get more consistent once there is regular movement in your life. Our minds need incremental growth, and any sudden shift only will bring on regression shortly after that, much like the yo-yo dieting cycle. Once walking enters your world, other movements will call to you eventually. Perhaps you will desire to do a childhood sport you used to enjoy, or you'll be ready for hitting the gym. Life will reveal the next new desire for some form of exercise. Following your passions and preferences will guide you to the best movements for your body and soul—movement and stillness equal emBODYment.

Finding your way

Walking wakes us up from the hypnosis of the old programs. Inherently integrative for the mind and body, walking will reveal your next steps to wellness. No grand purpose is necessary to be revealed, only to have walking in your life and all else remains the same, is enough. If there is no trust for anything else, you can trust movement. The same goes for stillness. I can attest how your life will not be the same growing these new habits in your world. Self-discovery lies in these two activities; intentional movement and stillness. "Easy does it," (another common AA phrase); stick with walking and stillness for as long as you like. Just those two things are enough for health to come to you.

Many of us were raised to believe we must fend for ourselves in this world. The sooner we figure out that fearful viewpoint only harms us, the sooner healing it can start. We are designed to help one other and own our right to feel well in this short life. Believe in the possibilities that live beyond your diagnoses and whatever conditions you present—your ability to heal lies dormant until it is activated. Find your way to wellness by tuning into your body and asking it what it needs. The next steps will be revealed if you remain open to answers. There are no hacks to real health. Slow and steady really does win the race. No shocks to the system are necessary. *Progress is a process; perfection is an illusion.* Serenity is built with the foundation of gratitude. Connect with understanding people who want your wellness as much as you do and let the upgrades begin.

Stillness in Action

Write out or make a voice recording of your answers for the inquiries:

- ✓ Forgiveness List: Think of all the things you can forgive yourself for.

- ✓ Addiction inventory: What addictions do you gravitate to? What basic need does it serve to satisfy? How does it relate to what you learned growing up? Can you envision a life doing something different? How would it feel to be free of it? What else would you do?

- ✓ Walking witness exercise: Explore your own company without any distractions, just you and a walk. Walk inside or outside your home, in the woods—any place where you can have solitude and feel safe exploring. Use all your five senses: smell, taste, touch, sight, and sound to stay present in the experience.

- ✓ Are there any areas of growth you are starting to desire? What needs do you have to facilitate that growth? Is there an existing community where you can get support? Pace yourself in your expectations.

Action in Stillness

- ✓ Stillness exercise (especially suited for restless people): Place any still focal point (a candle is ideal) before you as you sit in a chair or on the floor. Set a timer for three minutes and let yourself be antsy. Allow the small movements of scratching, stretching, and squirming without any condemnation whatsoever. Note what thoughts and feelings surface.

Action Initiative

- ✓ Look into support for your growth.

- ✓ Explore places, groups, and people to reach out to online or at your local town hall or community center to connect to resources and receive assistance for your growth.

11

How many will pass from the earth and how many will be created; who will live and who will die; who will die after a long life and who before his time;
who by water and who by fire,
who by sword and who by beast,
who by famine and who by thirst,
who by upheaval and who by plague,
who by strangling and who by stoning.
Who will rest and who will wander, who will live in harmony and who will be harried, who will enjoy tranquillity and who will suffer, who will be impoverished and who will be enriched, who will be degraded and who will be exalted.

- Unetannah Tokef, a Jewish liturgical poem

Chapter 11

Trinities of Health

"I trained four years to run nine seconds and people give up when they don't see results in two months."

—Usain Bolt

Process and pain

If the sleep meds, pain meds, iron supplements, and topical acne creams had worked, I probably wouldn't have traveled down this meandering road. If it weren't for my long, ongoing exploration in pursuit of the root causes of my multitude of uncomfortable symptoms, along with my struggles with bad habits, avoidant behavior and self-betrayal (aka addictions), I'd never have been led to my emPOWERment. *My pain contained my confidence and power.* My "pain in the neck" discomfort was a trigger and a gift. It allowed me to dig into my inner life, ultimately finding my purpose in serving others to support them in their health restoration. The process of understanding the factors that contributed to my chronic pain was often frustrating and confusing, but it led me to honor the rich layers of my being.

The true measure of wellness is "wellth"—for ourselves and the planet. Wealth fails to factor in health, but without it, we really have very little. Latest discoveries in science reveals that what is best for our wellth also happens to be what is best for the earth's ecology. As a result, demand for wellth and better production practices are skyrocketing. There is a call to bring balance to the bigger picture of well-fare for humans and the rest of the inhabitants in this world, including the earth itself. One person at a time is one step closer to shifting awareness into this necessary next paradigm of responsible and sustainable economies.

Two trinities to health: within and without

True personal health is the culminated by and reflected in the three internal aspects of our beingness; mental (mind), physical (body), and emotional (heart) well-being. External to our beingness, the factors that influence our individual wellness are our social, environmental, and spiritual health. *These outside influencers have a massive play in how healthy or unhealthy we are.* Of course, we can only control our own lives, so we must focus there, and the outside influences will shift as we do. Categorizing spiritual health as something outside ourselves is no accident. The spirit is something we connect to, but it is received through the heart (our emotions). Therefore, the space between the higher spirit and our personal emotions is the bridge between ourselves and beyond. Our spiritual connection is either conditioned into us or out of us in our development.

Culturally, I identify with the latter, having felt spiritually disconnected until I began to restore my health. I realize this division can be debatable because some believe we are alive with the gift of spirit inside of us. It is safe to say that many do not feel a spiritual reality until an outside occurrence connects to it. Let it be enough to leave it there.

Sensing something amiss spiritually evoked a desire to search for meaning in my life as a young person. I had a whispering curiosity, wanting to find meaning in my insignificant and neglected little existence. Mythology, legends, and fables were my first escape and my first curiosity when I was approaching adolescence. Discovering Goddesses gave me hope for strength and beauty, and Greek myths gave me metaphors about life. Aesop's fables gave me some wisdom that I didn't see in my day-to-day experience. The childish wonder may have planted the seed of growth, knowing that life was confusing and that someday I'd understand why it all unfolded as it did. From my perspective, something was off in the outside world, and my senses were strong about it.

Cultural progression

While my body developed physically through adolescence, the mental and emotional aspects went completely ignored. There was no nurturance of either of the two, but I craved it. For most people, that's the norm. Puberty happens to us, and we're left to deal with all the hormones and confusion of our meat-grinder post-industrial culture on our own. We are encouraged by society to avoid the pitfalls and taboos of self-destruction (like sex, drugs, and rock and roll) unless we happen to be raised with or identify with them. Physical development is on autopilot for our first rapid transformation beyond childhood. Puberty happens earlier and earlier in recent times and child obesity continues to soar. Mental and emotional issues during prepubescence is also more common than decades past. Dysfunction is louder than ever nowadays, and it's not only poor food quality to blame. Messages of imbalance seem to be everywhere, and the denial of its magnitude is impressive! Health illiteracy seems to be running rampant; why aren't there any answers but taking pills, trendy diets, and surgical procedures?

Matters of the body, mind, and heart

Let's get to breaking down the basics. The body is the physical self. It's tangible. We only have to use our senses to know it exists. The mind is a conceptual aspect of the brain. And the brain, greatly affected by the nutrients we take in, regulates our nervous and hormonal systems, impulses, thoughts, and beliefs based on memory and external stimuli. We cannot see the mind, but we know it resides inside of us. It's not hard to conceive of connecting with our minds and the minds of others. The heart is intangible in today's world, although we can tune into its beating if we put our hand over it. It is the least understood organ, more than a mere pump, having vital endocrine functions. The heart is our intuitive center. The emotions emit different frequencies, and we can sense them, often judging them as good or bad, depending on how they make our bodies feel. "Good" feelings like joy, happiness, and curiosity are higher and lighter in frequency, "bad" feelings like sadness, anger, and contempt are lower and denser. We can sense these frequencies in others as vibrations. Some are aware of this, and others are not, depending on how tuned in to their own heart and emotions they are.

Intuition is the heart's awareness of ours and other's emotional states and the ability to respond to them without any interference. The heart seems to be the second fiddle to the mind, but it's actually stronger than the mind and more vital to our health. We can live brain-dead. We can't live heart-dead. To connect to our hearts and the hearts of others feels intimate and often vulnerable. The non-profit, Heartmath Institute, a leading scientific research facility for heart-brain coherence discovered:

> "The heart is the most powerful source of electromagnetic energy in the human body, producing the largest rhythmic electromagnetic field of any of the body's organs. The heart's electrical field is about 60 times greater in amplitude than the electrical activity generated by the brain."[11]

The emotions that come alive in us dictate our neurological and hormonal responses. Whether in stress response or a relaxation response, our heart modulates our body's functioning, delivering blood and signaling hormones as needed to wherever demanded. Emotions are biologically based and serve essential functions; that is when they are not shut down, numbed or dysregulated (meaning a poor ability to manage emotional responses or to keep them within an acceptable range of typical emotional reactions). Perhaps it's my perspective here, but it seems that the topic of emotions themselves have been stigmatized, causing triggers of shame, guilt, and fear subconsciously for so many. I hope to normalize

---

[11] https://www.heartmath.org/research/science-of-the-heart/energetic-communication/

being fully human, removing that stigma, bringing in the next renaissance of emotional intelligence.

Emotions are as vital as any other aspect of ourselves, but they get minimized or criticized more often than not by many. Big feelings seem to slow things down, and most have little patience to manage their own emotions, let alone the emotions of others. The little "t" traumas everyone experiences attach to our relationships with emotions. How we judge them, is what makes them so hard to accept and manage. How emotions were responded to (or acted out dramatically) gets most people all squirmy when most folks broach the topic of emotional health. Remember, triggers are gifts. Dive into them and find your freedom. It's a shame not to prioritize emotional wellness, since mental and physical health are dependent on it. It is time to value the intangible aspects of our lives. Emotional regulation is the root of our vitality. Everything is out of whack when regulation is off, no matter how good-looking and healthy we appear on the surface.

The body is the sum of the mind and heart

The tangible (body/physiological), intangible (heart/emotional), and conceptual (mind/mental) aspects are constantly striving for harmony and balance. When imbalanced, like a tree modifies its growth path to better lean into the sunlight, humans adapt to less-than-ideal conditions and will lean on anything to achieve and maintain some semblance of balance. The manifestation of disease in the body is a clear and concise reflection of an imbalance in mind and/or heart. In all our anatomical attributes and flaws, beyond basic genetics like eye and hair color, our physique concisely reflects our beliefs and feelings, however aware or unaware.

Eczema on my face clearly expressed my gut, hormonal, and nervous system imbalances. Too much stress and too little rest threw my body off balance. The dis-eases we present on the outside leave a trail of clues that lead to the root causes if we track them. The adamantly perseverant and humble can resolve them, as I have.

Finally answers

After over two and a half years of intensive investigation of my skin and gut issues and after revealing the Hashimoto's diagnosis, I was able to put all my symptoms into remission in only a few of months with following a strict autoimmune regimen to eliminate all possible contributing factors. Being largely gluten-free, dairy-free wasn't enough, I tried the AIP diet (Auto-Immune Protocol) which was of zero help. Then the Low-Histamine diet gave me hope, as I found certain fruits and veggies were the cause of my flare ups on my face and with my arthritic pain. After many months of working with a functional medicine gastrointestinal doctor and her nutrition coaching team couldn't figure out what my root issue was, I became frustrated with cookie-cutter health treatment. Adding tons of supplements and ordinary dietary advice kept me stuck in the mud. I moved forward, knowing I had to dig deeper than they were capable. Thankfully, following the carnivore elimination diet helped me to resolve the war in my gut, the growing rash on my face, and restored my energy levels to normal. Desperate to try anything and ensure I had no room for error, I hired a carnivore coach which came with a community, and also two food-addiction groups. The support continues to keep me away from my drug-foods of flour, sugar, grains, nuts, and seeds. Perseverance and patience bring answers, I'm the poster child for that. Finding your own path and getting the right support specifically for you will get you to better health, the journey starts with building self-trust. Your inner-guidance is the leader in this, no one else.

Believe wellness can be had

The most prominent aspect of recovering from illnesses and imbalances is the unwavering belief that *it is possible to recover*. Plus, getting the proper support. When I say "proper," I mean the support aligned with your own individual needs, not the popular opinions of others. It is important to be as objective as possible, and it can be a pitfall to think we know what we need to later discover that wasn't the right solution. Venturing on the wellness journey is akin to scientific research, and we are a biological experiment. Trial and error will lead to answers. The health journey is not a straight shot, but a meandering road. If giving up is not an option, you will find the answers you seek.

Adventures are exploratory, the path of health is nothing short of a life adventure. Finding the right elements that suit you is as important as the desire to be healthy. No different from a hairstylist or a massage therapist, finding the proper help is a very personal relationship that influences how you experience the process. If the support doesn't resonate with you, recovery will undoubtedly fail and can create much frustration. Every supportive experience is a learning experience, contrasting what we need and what we don't need. So even if you got the wrong support at first, you just gained more clarity about what you're after. Have faith in the adventure that is your unique life.

Failing forward

What a powerful, triggering word in American society—failure. Yet, it is not the root of hopelessness. With the right perspective, failure can be reframed to reflect growth. Willingness to explore options in pursuit of dis-ease recovery creates resilience and grit, and there is no failure in that. Arriving at dead-ends fuels frustration, of course, and drives us to seek a new path. There IS a root cause or even several; there is no *effect* without a *cause*. If it's just your fate to feel unhealthy, you'd not be reading this book. Giving in to our illnesses is the only failure that can hurt us. Stumbling blocks are not failings, they are teachings. When hopelessness sets in, we feel trapped, and positive outcomes seem improbable. Then, depression locks us into our unhealthy beliefs and behaviors, and our dis-eases progress. Usually our dis-ease ends up killing us directly or indirectly.

People use excuses like "everyone has a vice" to enable their unhealthy habits. Not everyone has them! Everyone has temptations, but not everyone indulges in them. Another self-defeating phrase, "it is what it is!" Folks who are cultivating the most rewarding character traits of humility, patience, and determination quit using these self-defeating phrases. "That's just the way the cookie crumbles," is submissive and accepting defeat, with no hope for better outcomes. Limiting beliefs like this reinforce hopelessness, total irresponsibility, and inaction.

Remember, no one succeeds or heals in isolation. Trying to do so will lead to infinite dead-ends. Yes, we all need solitude to reflect and process our contrast and discover our preferences. Humans are designed to do things *collectively and collaboratively*. Modern hyper-individualism is the biggest rouse in developed countries like the United States. Most of us pretend not to need others because it is frowned upon to lean "too much" on others. We raise our kids to be independent but prematurely expect independence and emotional maturity. We use tough love where tenderness is needed. We learn that it's not safe to reach out and ask for help, being denied assistance over and over again. We learn to wallow in our disappointment. We get into this habit of hopelessness unless we feel the spark of inspiration and motivation.

The Inner-Alignment Formula

To encapsulate the heart, body, and mind relationship:

HEALTHY

Heart (Emotional) + Body (Physiological) + Brain (Mental) requires

PURE

Stillness + Movement + Nutrition respectively

Here's the relationship to each in detail:

Heart & Stillness

Presence lives in the heart. We come alive in presence and pause. People resist being still due to conditioning and a rushed sense that we are always running out of time. There is a lot of pressure to get things accomplished always. Yes, time is limited in this lifetime, but a rushed sensation is agitated, and letting that feeling be in the driver's seat of our actions isn't fair to our preferences. What do you want to do with these passing moments? The heart knows its exact preference. It knows only in the present moment and how it feels, regardless of our conscious awareness of it. A root cause of not being able to enjoy stillness is resistance and judgment of the feelings we have at the moment. Condemning our feelings is self-neglect at its core. The limiting beliefs that fuel our undoing emanate from this split of denial of what the heart feels to be true.

Agitation and condemnation are a lot of pressure and stress on our being. Becoming aware of heavy feelings stops us from reacting to them, so we can liberate ourselves from the stress of them. Our awareness enables us to clearly sense and illuminate what we need in any moment, instead of habitually bypassing the senses and letting the emotions dominate us. So practicing stillness develops our emotional regulation, accepting our senses and stressors, in observation our emotions, slowing down our response time to calmly choose a centered response. Feelings of agitation and anxiety usually come up in the first attempts of stillness and under it doubt, inadequacy, insecurity, and hopelessness, which usually ends the first few attempts at finding this "Zen" we are hoping to achieve. *There will be no Zen until we allow what is to be.* Zen is also not a permanent state of being, being realistic in our expectations. Bliss is just another emotion. Feeling dense emotional layers with the power of witness serve to teach us self-trust so we can settle into acceptance of the body however it is feeling at the time. Using breathwork is helpful to rest the heart's emotions, gaining better self-control by honoring ourselves exactly as we are and what we are feeling.

Stillness, like walking, is a greatly integrative exercise. Without judgment or condemnation, we settle into the body and observe the body's signals. All subtleties speak to us loudly. The tingling, itches, body pains, and discomforts ask for surrender to what is, not anticipate what should be. Learning to be still attunes the heart with the belly (sacral chakra), the gut instincts. No matter how short a length of time, showing up to practice stillness for even two or three full breaths programs the heart, our emotional center, to settle into the physical body. When the heart and body are in tune with and trust one another, a sense of safety and calm is restored.

Body & Movement

We all think we know everything on the topic and like to plug our ears when the word exercise is uttered. Many folks still do not know how exercise benefits more than the muscles and circulation. Exercise also strengthens skeletal, nervous, hormonal, immune, mental, and emotional functioning. Any low-impact exercise benefits the body in its entirety. Physical exercise's connection to the emotions and the mind is nothing short of intimate. Movement changes our heart rate and our chemistry and literally gets us emBODYed. Movement helps us to feel physically better. We all know it's good for us, but why is it so hard for so many to do? Too many of us are not accustomed to feeling well. It is our habituated feelings and beliefs that keep us in unwell states which we are familiar with instead of feeling the pleasure of moving our bodies. Starting with focusing on cultivating practicing stillness more and better nutrition will *naturally* get us to move, it's an organic process. When we have better inputs of calming our systems down and having better quality food, we urge to get moving. Start slow, or better, start stopped to move forward!

There can be no health without regular movement. To my sedentary friends, begin with nutrition, and the confusion will be sorted through gently and compassionately with self-awareness and support. Once we've gotten some good nourishment in the body and shave at with our emotions for a bit, we will get to moving. Starting with calming exercise is the best way to begin. Tension releasing exercises like the IMI method, walking, swimming, dancing, Tai chi, and Qi Gong all tone the vagus nerve, the regulatory core of the autonomic nervous system, allowing the "feel good" hormones to flood our bloodstream and bathe our brains. The continuous left-right action of walking and swimming bring balance to the brain's two hemispheres, regulating the endocrine glands inside our skull and throughout the rest of us.

Brain function and nutrition

Our beliefs are at the root of what we put in our mouths. You deserve to feel good, and any other belief is a learned lie. We are born to feel healthy, not ill. Nutrition is usually the main contributing factor when it comes to feeling unwell. We are what we eat, right? If we eat crap, we feel like it. Naturally, when we eat well, we will feel well. Our diet influences stress management in a big way, even more so than exercise. Pause for a few moments and inquire if you can imagine yourself feeling healthy and well, starting with envisioning eating a way of eating that gives you life instead of exhausting it.

What we thought was healthy was programmed into us. It's not your fault you eat what you do. What we believe is good for us originates in childhood. Popular mainstream conditioning impacted our preferences as we grew into our adolescence. Culture has an enormous influence on our intake. Our original beliefs in nutrition are passed down to us from our ancestors and their preferences are stored in our DNA! Many never deviate from their cultural conditioning and suffer the same consequences. We shift our dietary preferences only if we dislike what we were raised on and discover alternatives. Generations of food preferences were dictated by the food supply and also steered our cravings and proclivities. Because we are what we eat, and our DNA was formed by our parents' DNA, our nutritional proclivities originate from them. This can be modified with awareness, of course.

Seek food alternatives to break the genetic chain of predispositions for preventable dis-eases. For example, three out of four of my grandparents died of preventable dis-eases of lung cancer, heart dis-ease, and diabetes. The fourth was a gambler whose death is still unknown, since he fled from the family. I smoked, ate sugar, and ran away from my issues until they caught up to me. Just because our parents or grandparents were unhealthy is no excuse for us to be unhealthy too. Taking an inventory of what foods make us feel good after eating them and a list of foods that make us feel crappy will help us begin the customized journey to what we need on our menu to feel well. Substances that are good for us will give us energy and support our body's functioning. Foods that aren't good for us will take energy and invite dysfunction. Food and drink are the gateways to our energy. They weren't kidding when they said food is fuel. What are you putting in your gas tank?

The chaotic world of nutritional guidance is complex, ever-changing, and always up for lively debate. Dietary paths must to be customized. There are no one-size-fits-all answers. Refined foods offer no real value other than comfort and pleasure. Generally, refined and processed "food" is crap, so start there. Find your substitutes first and then acclimate and congratulate yourself on some huge progress. I highly recommend aiming for reducing sugar products and refined carbohydrates. Clarity comes quick with that shift alone.

Now that there is some understanding how our bodies work in an integrated way, we can begin to explore how things got so confusing in the world of nutrition. As we fail forward through this human evolution many are learning only recently what true health always was and is returning to be.

Stillness in Action

Explore how long it might realistically take to restore your health. What is required to prepare for the process of your health restoration?

- ✓ Dense emotion release practice: Shake your arms when you feel heavy and are experiencing uncomfortable feelings. Standing up and jumping for about twenty seconds while shaking your arms is even better. Shaking your body releases dense emotions that are surfacing.

- ✓ Dense emotion acceptance practice: Sit with the dense feelings and fully honor them without criticism. You can do this in place of the release activity or combine it and do it afterward or beforehand. Witness the sensations without tracing them to any root cause. Do not try to fix the feeling or find a better feeling, be fully with each feeling exactly as it arrives, as if each feeling was a visiting guest.

- ✓ Nutrition inventory and goals: List "feel bad" and "feel good" foods and drinks and the effects of each.

Action in Stillness

- ✓ After the dense emotion practices, allow your body to process the emotion without the help of your thoughts. Take a bath, casually read a book, listen to some relaxing music, and let yourself be exactly as you are with nothing to do.

Action Initiative

✓ Cultivating being and releasing practices makes for powerful shifts in awareness. Do both shaking and sitting practices every day, any time of day, once a day for seven days. Don't forget to set reminders and commit to your practices to discover the growth that ensues.

12

Let food be thy medicine,
And let medicine be thy food.

—Hippocrates 460 BC-370 BC

Chapter 12

Nutrition: Past, Present & Future

"The history of government regulation of food safety is one of watchdogs chasing the horse after it's out of the barn."
—David Kessler, MD, FDA Commissioner from 1990-1997

What is personal is political

What we eat has consequences on the supply chains of production. The good news is that eating well is best for the world. Corporate food businesses will adapt to the demands of its consumers or they won't survive. Peering around the grocery stores, we can see how our food choices are changing what is offered. We, as consumers, have the power to dictate what to take into our bodies. Food quality is the key to better health not only personally, but also ecologically, ethically, and sustainably. Briefly, I'll guide you through nutrition through the ages.

Our first food supply, naturally wild and all organic

Homo sapiens, were primitive in its dawn. Until about 12,000 years ago, humans were nomadic hunter-gatherers and survived that way for eons.[12]

Gathering (aka foraging) was a vital part of survival, before we learned how to plant seeds. Figuring out what was safe and what was toxic to ingest had its consequences and became a crucial part of our development. Some tribes were accustomed to more gathering, and some more hunting, depending on whatever was more plentiful. Managing constant food scarcity dictated our days. Obesity was rare because of the need to move in search of nourishment. Food security did not exist: securing food for the day, month, and season was the main purpose and all cultural norms came out of that. The future, always unknown, was a mystery of life.

After the first technological advance, making fire, which occurred between one and two million years ago, revolutionized how we ate. At this time, humans were savage in preparing food, primally eating raw. The average lifespan was twenty-five to thirty.[13]

Then, only ten to twelve thousand years ago, humans all over the world began to shift from hunter-gather societies to agrarian, causing many cultures to settle down, needing to be less nomadic.[14] Storing and keeping food created a sense of security never fathomed before. Of course, tribal and territorial warring

---

[12] https://www.oxfordhandbooks.com/view/10.1093/oxfordhb/9780199569885.001.0001/oxfordhb-9780199569885

[13] Caspari R, Lee SH. Is human longevity a consequence of cultural change or modern biology? *Am J Phys Anthropol.* 2006;129(4):512–517. doi:10.1002/ajpa.20360

[14] study.com/academy/lesson/the-agricultural-revolution-timeline-causes-inventions-effects.html

prevented any certainty, but it was still quite an improvement from what was before. Life spans varied dramatically, but people could live as long as fifty or sixty, but most lived between thirty-five and forty.[15]

The wheel advancement happened only between six and eight thousand years ago, allowing the transportation of foods with more ease and quantity.[16] Ships were the last major advancement less than six thousand years ago when trains, automobiles, and planes in the last century revolutionized the trading of goods globally.[17]

Viewing the progress of humanity through this wide lens, any grade-schooler would agree that politics throughout history was largely concerned with territorial pursuits. The rigid hierarchical worldview permitted countless unethical crimes to humanity in the name of religion and "civilization." Rationales to steal and destroy other cultures' food and other resources were a part of it all—such gravely insecure and unsettling times for so many humans all through time.

For thousands of years, violence and hostility were normal, and avoiding them was our MO. Our minds impeccably evolved to minimize danger and maximize safety in light of brutality thrust upon groups of people. We ate what was available; options were few before civilization became sophisticated by trading goods between cultures.

Nutrition evolution

---

[15] https://www.verywellhealth.com/longevity-throughout-history-2224054

[16] https://www.smithsonianmag.com/science-nature/a-salute-to-the-wheel-31805121/

[17] https://www.britannica.com/technology/ship/History-of-ships

Grains were first discovered while foraging. Wheat berries were eaten raw or cooked until grinding became widely used over 75,000 years ago.[18] The Agrarian Revolution brought with it the concept of civility. Hunter-gather societies became known as civilizations, whereas before, they were referred to as tribes. It became considered uncivilized to be nomadic, a rationale for much genocide. Alcohol dates back almost ten thousand years ago, as we became civilized in agrarian times, accidentally from the fermentation of stored grain.[19] Bread slowly emerged into existence twenty to eight thousand years ago, and cheese was accidentally discovered about five thousand years ago.[15] Sugar exploded after its invention throughout the post-Christ era, rapidly spreading all over the world to keep up with demand. As massive diversity in diets grew, waistlines also grew. Populations flourished, but so did dis-ease. Still, food security was as safe as its civilization, threats were common, and so was hostile conflict. Along with the proliferation of sugar consumption, diabetes came onto the scene during the 11th century; insulin revolutionized its treatment of this "sweet" dis-ease around 1923.[20]

Excessive consumption of alcohol, sugar, and refined carbohydrates like bread was commonplace with the introduction of each. Minus plagues and famines, human populations grew massively all over the world, danger and insecurity always being a concern as threats to survival came and went. The genetic predispositions to overindulge are easily seen in this context. Gifts

---

[18] https://wheatworld.org/wheat-101/wheat-facts/

[19] Rosso, A. (2012). Beer And Wine In Antiquity: Beneficial Remedy Or Punishment Imposed By The Gods? *Acta Medical History*, 10(2);237—262.

[20] https://www.thediabetescouncil.com/diabetes-before-and-after/

to the world as they may have been, these advances in food and drink are where civilization took a turn for the worse, from a health perspective, creating generations of the most common preventable dis-eases like heart disease, obesity, hormonal disorders, and digestive issues.

The first industrial revolution

In the 18th century, the developing world's mechanization grew in efficiency. Factory work flourished, and so did the widespread use of coffee and tea. Humans, whether free or enslaved, were treated like machines. The assembly line mindset created a rushed and pressured lifestyle. Time was of the essence, and the punch clock spread all over the developed world. Stimulating drugs found their favor, and evidence supports that one of the first sodas had caffeine, cocaine, and sugar in it in 1886.[21]

In 1958, diabetes cases were less than one percent of the US population. In 2015, it jumped to over seven percent, and the CDC calculated the US as having over twenty-three million cases. Only three years later, crude estimates report thirteen percent of adults had diabetes in the USA.[22,23] More than one out of ten people in the US have diabetes now. Globally, trends are similar.[24] The availability and access to sugar and processed foods is now the problem for many humans in the developed world, not a lack of nutrient-dense food. The industrial boom brought food security,

[21] https://www.livescience.com/41975-does-coca-cola-contain-cocaine.html
[22] https://www.cdc.gov/diabetes/statistics/slides/long_term_trends.pdf
[23] https://www.cdc.gov/diabetes/pdfs/data/statistics/national-diabetes-statistics-report.pdf
[24] https://www.washingtonpost.com/national/health-science/diabetes-becoming-alarmingly-common-worldwide-new-study-finds/2011/06/24/AGMkaFlH_story.html

now excess is our main dilemma. This excess can be seen as a form of malnutrition.

Post-Industrial revolution

Between the first and second world wars, there was a proliferation of food companies. Grocery stores bloomed while village markets died out. Grocery stores were invented at the beginning of the 19th century, along with the invention of refrigeration.[25] You could buy all you needed at one store instead of going to individual bakers, butchers, and village markets. Convenience foods flooded the market. Preservatives, like vegetable oil, started to be added to all processed food stocking the shelves. After World War II, shelf life and cooking easy recipes with preprepared ingredients, like cooked, canned beans, Jell-o and pudding mixes, and dehydrated rice, gained in demand.[26]

Unheard of until then, snacking budded in the mid-50s as the invention of wonder bread and mini-cakes, and pies. Sugar started to be added to processed foods, and we couldn't get enough of them. Humans began to eat more and more food "products."

Snack-food revolution

The obsession with snack "treats" continued into the late 20th century with Ding-Dongs, Twinkies, individually sized chips, and plenty of other cheap snacks and sodas. These treats were marketed as rewards for a job well done, as they are now. Being good merits a treat (because we *deserve* it, after all). Pop culture glamorized gum, soda, and all the rest of the quick-fix food

---

[25] https://time.com/4480303/supermarkets-history/#
[26] Gosse, Van; Moser, Richard (2008). *The World the Sixties Made: Politics and Culture in Recent America.* p. 150

products. "Double your pleasure, double your fun!" Marketing was as sexy as ever, pushing low-quality products onto consumers. A focus on low-fat diets at the latter end of the century ignored that excess carbohydrates were just as bad as sugary snacks. Gary Taubes, journalist and author of *What If It's All Been A Big Fat Lie?*, revealed from a series of the CDC's National Health Examination surveys that up until the end of the '70s, obesity rates stayed between 12-14 percent then jumped up to 22-25 percent. For some reason, fat was demonized while sugar got off scot-free. The US Sugar Lobby intentionally downplayed the link between sugar and heart dis-ease. In fact, there's evidence that supports the sugar industry suppressing the harmful effects of sugar, pulling a bait and switch with fat.[27,28]

Type 2 diabetes was linked to sugar and refined carb intake, so companies boasted that sugar alternatives were safe but weren't. Lead was the first sugar replacement in the Middle Ages, so there's the kickstart to the madness. Saccharin, another known poison, was popular in the late 1800s. Although it was taken off the US market in 1981, the ban on it was lifted in 2000.[29] The healthiest alternatives to regular sugar are natural sugars, as chemical sugars only confuse the body.[30]

---

[27] https://jamanetwork.com/journals/jamainternalmedicine/article-abstract/2548255
[28] https://www.foodnavigator.com/Article/2016/09/13/How-the-sugar-lobby-paid-scientists-to-point-the-finger-at-fat-JAMA
[29] https://www.ncbi.nlm.nih.gov/pmc/articles/PMC3198517/
[30] https://www.mayoclinic.org/healthy-lifestyle/nutrition-and-healthy-eating/in-depth/artificial-sweeteners/art-20046936#

The tech revolution

Current day, in the context of food alone, it's the age of confusion and anxiety. After the internet brought instantaneous products, services, and knowledge to people, people can get anything they want by pressing a few buttons on their smartphones at any time of day or by driving to the closest gas station. Food choices are now infinite at any time, almost any place in the world, thanks to food delivery companies. Pre-made meals of any kind; vegan, vegetarian, paleo, keto, carnivore, raw, low carb, and Mediterranean are diverse and many. With the world's food at our fingertips, what are we choosing with such amazing power? Our health or our dis-ease?

The elitist organic lie

It's an outright lie and stereotype that organic food is only for people who can afford it. Access to healthy food is not exclusively for wealthy people. If food products are cheap, there is a reason for it. I have lived on an hourly wage for most of my life and have been buying exclusively organic for decades. It's a choice. Cost is a prevalent reason to avoid shifting towards eating organic foods, and it's not true. Being pretty tight on the food budget is more about priorities than expenses. Generic labels are cost-effective, and so is buying what is in season and on sale. What indulgences do you have money to spend on in your life? Your priorities in spending speak to what you truly value. Try gradually replacing non-organic foods with organic ones. Sometimes you might have to pass on what is overpriced and get the discounted similar food instead. Flexibility helps when it comes to maximizing your organic food budget.

It's time to cut the crap

If you lack wellness and want to feel better, decide to transition to nutrient-dense food and cut the processed foods. That is where to begin. Forget about low-carb and keto initiatives if you still drink tons of soda and eat sweets and snack foods. It's too big of a jump. Slowly move into more whole foods and when you're used to that, continue deeper into the world of nutritional eating. If it's overwhelming to start there, get support. The truth is, most of us are never "ready," which is why starting now is as good a time as any. Get help. That's the first step. Being honest with ourselves is the path to restoration. Be brave, explore and learn to reach out. A bazillion resources lie in the wait of your clicks and calls. Of course, I'm one of those resources, but I may not be the right fit for you. Finding the right support, the avenues that feel best to you, are precisely where you belong. Any other place is not the right place. Don't forget to notice that inner-critic who finds fault with everyone and see if you can't get past that hyper-critical voice who wants to keep you stuck where you are now. If you're not feeling your best, you know you don't want to stay there. Moving on requires only curiosity. Take a peek into your next upgrade.

Foodwise, the goal I usually advocate, is to reduce inflammation with anti-inflammatory foods to become healthy and well. Find out what foods create inflammation in your body. The worst inflammatory foods are sugar, coffee, fried, processed, and refined foods. See what blocks you from cutting those foods out as if you were doing a social experiment. What comes up? What beliefs, people, occasions, feelings, or pressures stop you? If tomorrow is the day you'll always begin, when will that day finally come?

To find one's own nutritionally aligned food path is to simply trust one's gut—literally and figuratively. We begin by finding the resources we are drawn to. Blood tests will support what direction to go from there regarding the best foods for our betterment and health restoration. Elimination diets can be helpful for this, under the advisement of a health professional who knows your specific health details. Figuring out one's food sensitivities is another place I always advocate beginning the journey. Having a ton of food sensitivities is a symptom of an underlying gut imbalance, so enter into it as if you were a scientist, investigating your own personal experiment that is your miraculous body.

Tragically, most mainstream medicine is incentivized by pharmaceutical companies and uses outdated scientific research, often funded by the giants of processed food businesses. There is utter confusion based on the conflicts between the big food industry's profits and people's health. The only way to find clarity is to follow your intuition, real data (personalized testing), and the latest discoveries in nutritional education.

Returning to organic, sustainable food cultivation

The next era in nutrition is in sustainable organic agriculture and responsible and ethical livestock management. There is a global movement upon us that has been going on since people started to realize that industrialized, high chemical input agriculture was not healthy for anyone at the dawn of the return to organically grown foods began in the early 1960s. Regenerating and restoring our earth's balance lies in our soil. *We can resolve the climate crisis through responsible food cultivation.* Buying locally grown, organic, responsibly raised and humanely treated animal and plant foods (free-range and grass-fed) is worth the investment for your health and the wellness of the planet. Granted, there are other concerns of global health pertaining to waste and pollution, but we can start healing it by nourishing the soil of its needed components instead of robbing the nutrients from it with chemical fertilizers and pesticides. With healthy soil comes carbon sequestration, which is the bridge to thriving, sustainable future economies.

In 2015, The International Research Institute for Agriculture, Food, and the Environment (INRAE), the largest food and environmental research organization in Europe, introduced at the UN Climate Change Conference an initiative called Four per One Thousand to enrich .4 percent of organic matter each year. If all countries agree, we can be carbon neutral by 2030! More details about it can be found at https://4p1000.org/. Our soil is the foundation of a sustainable future. Proper resource and waste management will bring us into this next wellness paradigm as needed for the survival of our species. Sustainable global economies will deliver order and harmony of resource management, the opposite of the impending doom of chaos and mayhem of unregulated waste and poorly managed resources. An apocalyptic prophecy is only one outcome, which is the result of corruption and greed, where you spend your money fuels either outcome. Which future do you want to foster?

A global health (r)evolution is dawning now. I cordially invite you to be a part of it. The decisions you make today fuel the outcomes of tomorrow.

Stillness in Action

Write down your awareness of your ancestral health:

- ✓ What are the dis-eases that run in your family? What nutrition or stresses do you believe may be related to your family members' health or lack thereof?

- ✓ Are there any adjustments to your current diet that would improve your health? What would it look like if you could create any strategy to adjust your diet?

Action in Stillness

Visualize your vibrant health:

- ✓ How does it feel? How are you spending your day? What activities do you see yourself doing?

- ✓ Picture what vibrant health looks and feels like to you.

Action Initiative

- ✓ If you are serious about feeling healthier, pair up with an "accountability buddy" or a life coach to help you strategize a sensible plan to get you on your way. Act now, and don't delay it another day. Your vibrant health awaits.

13

"*Love and compassion are necessities, not luxuries. Without them, humanity cannot survive.*"

- Dalai Lama XIV (1935-present)

Chapter 13

Corporations That Care

"He who cannot be a good follower, cannot be a good leader."
—Aristotle

Returns on investment

People want to work where they are valued. The COVID pandemic caused a shift in the job market that reverberated through the developed world. Suddenly, the topic of work culture came into focus as companies and employees were forced to accept unavoidable circumstances and did their best to survive. Amidst the lockdowns and shelter-in-place mandates, employees began to prioritize their stress levels.

Companies who care about their employees and value their well-being see considerable returns in team member loyalty and retention rates. Places of business that provide a harmonious balance of psychological safety, fostering creativity, and leadership development thrive over the old fear-based model of domination and subordination. There is immense value in the wellness of human capital, in a word, performance. Favoring ingenuity and offering mutual respect to the workforce enhances and exponentiates performance. Inattentive old dinosaurs who subjugate and aren't capable of camaraderie are quickly dying out. The next evolution is businesses require a thriving, psychologically safe workplace. Nowadays, caring is not some Kumbaya concept that has no merit in the industry; it is vital to its success. Forward-thinking companies with a vested interest in the health of their workers are leading us into tomorrow. People work better when they're healthier. That's the bottom line. The American Psychological Association states that unhappy workplaces increase depression and heart disease risks.[31] We owe it to ourselves and our teams to do better than that.

Corporations lead culture

The government's role is not leadership but to uphold leaders among the populace. Politicians and policymakers serve to implement policies that special interests and organizations call for. What upgrades and modernizes political procedures and priorities is the *demand* for progress. Where national and global growth and wellness are concerned, priorities are set by cultural leadership. Since the dawn of humanity, cultural advancement has led to social progress and technology. Ingenuity drives culture, technology, and art forward.

---

[31] https://www.apa.org/monitor/2010/12/morale

Since they have the power of wealth and status, businesses have the greatest influence on what the government focuses on. The leaders of businesses and their valuing of health and wellness of their business culture and their human capital is changing culture today. Change will always be a constant, as in the past relating to the progress in the workplace; emancipation of enslaved people, child labor laws, and women's rights drastically changed the working lives of people and society at large. The health of people falls greatly on workplace culture. It has become the responsibility of employers to foster wellness awareness and initiatives for their employees to be healthier. Selecting healthcare programs that support employees to maximize their wellness offers lower insurance premiums. Today's healthcare companies are heavily incentivized to lower their expenses by investing in improving people's lives instead of merely covering hospital and doctor's visit costs. The health of the worker and the business's overall health create a win-win no-brainer dynamic where it would be counter-intuitive to not invest in staff wellness programs.

Business health is people health

There is a direct connection between team member well-being and business well-being. When staff isn't feeling well emotionally, mentally, or physically they are more disengaged and miss more workdays per year. According to Willis Towers Watson's 2020 Global Benefits Attitudes Survey, one in seven employees report issues of wellbeing. They are four times more likely to be disengaged and miss 12 or more days of work per year.[32] More and

---

[32] https://www.wtwco.com/en-US/Insights/2021/02/covid-19-requiring-employers-to-step-up-expand-well-being-programs

more businesses that provide healthcare to their employees are offering programs like free gym memberships to foster well-being. The climate of culture today demands support for people's health, and it's a win-win for all. Companies with the best benefits like Starbucks, Netflix, HubSpot, Amazon, and Google are bringing staff healthcare to the next level.[33]

Wellness incentives support individuals in developing their personal health. Companies not only have a vested interest in preventing injuries and burnout but can also improve team member loyalty by offering mental health services. Today's best businesses offer gym and educational tuition reimbursement. Incentivizing free annual checkups for medical and dental is a standard of supporting staff to stay vigilant toward their health journey rather than ignoring it. A business that offers a Health Savings Account (HSA) will match their employee's investment in vitamins, fitness classes, health supplies, and out-of-network providers as a cash-based debit card.

Feel good, live better

Vidal Sassoon chimed in with their catchy slogan in the 1980s, "When you look good, you feel good." Of course, this is all good if you're selling beauty products. The opposite is more accurate, *"When you feel good, you look good."* Vitality makes you radiant, not products. Any size or shape, when a person feels healthy and well, they have a better perspective on life. As I mentioned earlier, nutrition is the fastest way and the first step to feeling better. Next, body movement maintains health, which can be achieved with

---

[33] https://www.betterup.com/blog/best-job-benefits

simple basics and low-impact. The payoffs are immense, so any block to the health needs to be addressed and not tolerated. Naturally, businesses that foster this wellness mindset orientation lead to healthier work cultures.

Upon the first interview, a company's hiring representative should take an interest in a candidate's well-being. Healthy people cope with stress with more grace, manage challenges better, and have higher morale. That is a positive sign of a company's wellness initiatives.

The value of emotional intelligence

Crucial to team leadership is a vested interest in promoting emotional intelligence development, allowing more psychological safety in their working world. Emotional intelligence affects emotional resilience, conflict, and stress management and is critical to maximizing job performance. Emotional intelligence (EI) in the workplace has five components; according to Daniel Goleman, the psychologist who popularized it, they are self-awareness, self-regulation, motivation, empathy, and social skills.[34] Whether in a leadership role or not, understanding how our emotions and actions affect others makes us more effective and healthful. Investing in EI delivers many positive returns.

Hands on tools

Providing stress-reducing resources in the office makes a huge difference in managing work-related problems and conflicts. Encouraging taking activity and mental breaks creates an atmosphere of stress reduction. Regular social events and

---

[34] https://www.mindtools.com/pages/article/newLDR_45.htm

platforms let coworkers get to know each other and can alleviate feeling isolated on the job. Having a small private room to take a meditation break helps calm people's nerves when they need it most. Flexible hours instead of rigid shifts, project-oriented deadlines instead of clock-based work create a life after the factory-line concept. Open spaces for breath breaks, stretching, and rest are vital to calm and smooth operations to foster productivity and high morale. Businesses that value investing in wellness reap the benefits in their day-to-day operations, growth, and bottom line.

Stillness in the workplace

When people feel overwhelmed, confused, or frustrated, they may experience destructive thoughts of quitting, giving up, and doing things half-assed. *That's when it's time for a break.* In the "Breath-Body Breaks," I train people to get them out of their heads and into their bodies. Set a timer or look at a clock and commit to a few minutes; even one minute is enough if you are new at stillness. The present moment is calming when we claim it and let our concerns and heavy emotions shift into the background for a few moments.

Here are a few ways to practice stillness for beginners:

- Two basic types of breathwork; 1) energy building, observing the breath moving in and out of the nose, and 2) tension releasing, observing the breath moving in the nose and out of the mouth. Use the energy building breath for more mental clarity and stimulation, emphasizing and lengthening the inhalation. For calming stress reduction, use the tension releasing breath, accentuating, and lengthening the exhalation. To keep the science of the physiology of it simple: inhalation increases the heart rate while exhalation decreases it.

- Two calming practices use patterned counting. My favorite is called the Square Breath. This is how you do it: Inhale to the count of four, hold at the top for four counts, exhale to the count of four, and hold at the bottom for four more counts. Speaking or thinking of one or two simple words like "inhale/peace" during the inhale and "exhale/stress" during the exhale is a very effective method to calm the nerves and rejuvenate the mindset. I often say "in" (inhaling) and "out" (exhaling). Use any words that support your intention to recharge or to release. They can be opposite, like in-love/out-fear, or complimentary, like in-calm/out-acceptance.

- Two focusing practices that I find immensely comforting are watching the flame of a candle flicker for as long as you like or use your senses to focus on the present moment by having a small object in your hand like a stone. You may hear the vibration of a slow drum (on audio), hear the leaves on the trees rustle outside your window, feel the breeze on your face from a fan, taste the residue of your drink in your mouth, smell a scented candle, feel the fabric your shirt, or recognize the weight of the glasses on your face.

Starting with one to three minutes of any of these exercises will help cultivate and maintain a more calming presence for the rest of the day. I always recommend committing to stillness once at the start of the day and again before bed. Setting recurring daily appointment reminders will give you the cue. Once it alarms, get to your stopping point of the project you're on and take care of yourself as the most important aspect of your day. Such a small exercise has so many benefits, including blood pressure and stress hormone regulation, so you feel less pressure and frustration with growing centeredness and a refreshed perspective.

Movement in the workplace

Taking movement breaks is *vital* to feeling good throughout the day. Too many people are in front of a computer for most of their time. Getting up and moving around every thirty minutes is essential, even only to stand up and move your joints for a few minutes. Sitting stagnant for hours leads to achiness, strained muscles, and exhaustion, leading to repetitive injuries like carpal tunnel, neck, and back issues.

Group challenges can be a fun way to inspire employees to get moving. Group classes and competitions connect teams and prevent social isolation at work. Some people love it; others are averted by it. Giving employees ideas and letting them decide what is best for them fosters positive work cultures. Challenges, where employees can privately track their progress instead of making it public, will avoid comparison. Health is purely individual, and comparison only makes those struggling feel worse. Inclusivity is key to progress. Removing all barriers to exercise must be considered when implementing wellness initiatives for physical activity.

Utilizing floor spaces for yoga, office-friendly exercise, and stretching maintains a proactive, health-positive attitude in the office. Walking and climbing stairs are always the easiest options for those who feel super self-conscious, shy, or reluctant to engage in group dynamics. Little actions add up. Even if people move around inside the office or circle the building once or twice (fresh air is powerfully revitalizing), breaks from sitting and feeling couped up alleviate stress and tension.

The IMI method's benefits in leadership training are building trust and confidence among teams while giving people personal tools for exercise breaks inside and beyond work. The method trains individuals in emotional intelligence, self-awareness, and inner-focus, which supports a psychologically safe and healthy workplace.

Ergonomics as a bridge to wellness

Good posture and proper body mechanics at work are not new concepts, but their significance has expanded. Aside from preventing repetitive injuries and minimizing body pain and fatigue, practicing better alignment at work is an opportunity for people to tune into their bodies as a habit. Most ergonomics companies focus on selling furniture and equipment to maximize work performance and reduce work-induced suffering. Buying the most ergonomically-correct furniture is useless if people aren't practicing better posture and body positioning. To get people working at their best, it is vital to learn how to use equipment and accessories with awareness *and train people how to care for themselves as they work.* Once self-care habits are instilled, people are motivated and empowered to better their wellness, and work quality naturally benefits.

Physical alignment is crucial when using office furniture and accessories, which is why most efforts fail to reduce repetitive injuries and incidents of tension headaches, and other chronic muscular pain and discomfort. Implementing the training of better postural habits and body mechanics and teaching tension-releasing exercises alleviates the constant tension and physical pain that affects so many working people minute by minute, week to week, and year after year.

Using ergonomics and physical alignment to arouse intrigue in chronic pain sufferers delivers kinesiology (the study of human movement) so that body awareness becomes a personal responsibility instead of their chair or desk set-up. The work equipment acts as reminders, but the habits that support alignment are the missing piece to well-being in the workplace.

Workplace peace of mind

The foundation of wellness in business environments is to have a psychologically safe place to empower and encourage individuals to take care of themselves while at work. The aim is to eradicate the weirdness factor of taking care of oneself. Breath breaks need to be as encouraged and expected as cigarette breaks (if not more so) and herbal tea to coffee. Stretching or having a moment of stillness at one's desk or breakroom is becoming normalized in many workplaces. Seeing coworkers rubbing their temples is now more a sign of health rather than overload.

The old business paradigm reveals outdated and unhealthy habits that used to be normal. Leading the responsibility shift in work cultures from enabling unwellness toward fostering vibrant healthfulness in the workplace by making healthier habits more appealing. There is no glory in being a workaholic or drinking a pot of coffee daily. Freely advocating mental breaks and time off helps people prevent accidents, injuries, and burnout and creates a community and collaboration. Corporations thrive as a social and living structure when not based on the old exploitative standard. Mutual benefit is the next paradigm. Finally, business is called to move toward realistic output expectations for long-term gain instead of squeezing results out of their teams, creating burnout and low staff retention rates.

Maybe for the first time in history, we are normalizing the health and well-being of businesses and the human capital that are its bones. Amplifying the well-being of the workforce is now the foundation of a business' strength. The recent COVID-19-induced job market shifts caused the power to tip into the employee's favor. Businesses need to compete for talented workers, expand their benefits packages, and address the personal needs of their teams. The tides are shifting—exactly as they need to be. Moving culture toward health and wellness can only transpire by necessity, precisely where we find ourselves today. David Rockefeller, a third-generation investment banker, explained how markets changed when he said, "If necessity is the mother of invention, discontent is the father of progress."

Bad businesses grow ill health

Minus the industries and businesses that profit from it, dis-ease drains efficiency and economy. The focus on wellness brings a win for everyone but those who profit from unwellness. Big tobacco diversified by investing in big food in the 1980s when cigarette sales began to drop. They started marketing more to kids with cartoon-like graphics and youthful models having fun to attract new smokers at a younger age. Today, big tobacco still markets nicotine to kids in different forms: e-cigarettes and vaporizers. Their investments in food, not surprisingly, were in processed snack foods, focusing their marketing on children with sugary drinks like Tang, Hawaiian Punch, and Kool-Aid. Phillip Morris owns Kraft Foods, and RJ Reynolds owns General Mills. So, instead of mere lung cancer deaths, they invested in creating more people with diabetes. It's common to go from tobacco addiction to food, as I did myself. I also gained sixty pounds in doing so. Companies like these capitalize on and encourage the addictive impulse.

Supporting the flourishing wellness economy

Those who profit from illness will eventually transition into better companies or be tossed aside like the last generation of old electronics. The financial benefits of wellness are starting to flourish. Lowering health insurance premiums is only one perk. Having happier workers transfers into better productivity, higher sales, and fewer work-related health problems. The wellness movement is leading the way, and smart leaders are following.

Corporations and large organizations have replaced the old villages and tribes of yesterday. They are the epicenter of our sustenance, indirectly providing shelter, safety, and food security. Families and communities, although important to thriving, are less vital to meeting our basic needs for survival because we need to earn money to provide for ourselves. Companies and organizations that consider their contribution to society's progress will benefit in the unfolding of future generations.

Health and wellness goals are not just a win-win, but a win-win-win. The achievement of health progress creates better alignment between individuals and the groups they influence by sharing it with others and creating a healthy, sustainable planet. This reality can be threatening to those who aren't in it for all to win and instead see life as an opportunity to exploit the "losers" as if they are among the "Us" (winners) group, versus "Them" (losers). The great illusion is that divide right there. There is no Them, it's only Us. Collaboration and respect are how we win the sustainable future. It's happening as we speak (well, as I write, and as you read).

The formula for the future is this:

Win for Self + Win for Others = Win for the Planet

Wellth = Wealth. Everyone wins. Imagine that.

Stillness in Action

Write down the ideas you have for building a better work culture for yourself and others:

- ✓ What would you like to envision for your business as far as health upgrades are concerned? What recommendations or actions can you take to lead your business towards a healthier work culture?

- ✓ What exercise and stillness practices can you incorporate into your workday, and when? Set your reminders for them every day you work, putting yourself on the priority list to improve your work morale and overall health. It's a daily INVESTment that will pay you back in dividends.

- ✓ Are there some ergonomic improvements to be made in your workspace? List them and take them to your office manager or human resources team. What body-mechanical improvements do you think might reduce pain and strain? Your company has a vested interest in preventing injuries and boosting your work performance and should be happy to pay for reasonable ergonomic upgrades. They can give me a call so I can ensure the upgrades will be effectively utilized.

Action in Stillness

- ✓ Take a few minutes to envision the ideal workplace and your ideal health. Keep daydreaming about it every day for as long as it takes to take action in moving towards those goals.

Action Initiative

✓ This week, create a health accountability partner or a community at work for regular walking sessions, stair climbing breaks, and/or a nutrition-based challenge. Be a leader in your workplace for everyone's wellness.

14

*"If they're ready, you can't say anything wrong.
If they're not ready, you can't say anything right."*

- March 1988, Sharon H, AA Grapevine

Chapter 14

Ready or Not

"So often in life, things that you regard as an impediment turn out to be great good fortune."
—Ruth Bader Ginsberg

Are you ready for wellness?

Change seems to happen to us more often than we seek it out. The pressing desire toward pleasure and repulsion of pain makes readiness a symptom of necessity. People and businesses only ever change when they have no other choice. That's survival and evolution. As far as my own growth is concerned, if it weren't for my exhaustion, multitudes of symptoms, and relentless curiosity, I'd never have been led to my inner-strength and restorative empowerment. I was never ready for change; I was driven by the necessity of it.

If insanity is doing the same thing and expecting a different result, then the source of our sanity is our lack of emotional awareness. When there is awareness of the problem but not the solution, we are stuck in the mud, feeling trapped and powerless. Pretending we are powerful when we are stuck is the epitome of denial and blind arrogance. I knew it too well. Humility is vital to growth and creating new supportive patterns to maintain wellness. Admitting we don't have answers opens the window to receive them. Potential solutions surface when we reach a point of standstill, a circumstantial pause (maybe divine intervention). Any way that creates a new direction is often the path of least resistance.

Shortly after committing to writing this book, I came upon a huge, ugly, scary block. The book's topic is emBODYment and emPOWERment, while I suffered from addictions to caffeine, sugar, and empty carbs. It made me feel disingenuous and like a fraud. "It's only caffeine" and "It's no big deal" were popular thoughts I clung to before. I had to humble myself and now know better, especially after writing about the topic of releasing my addictions. I wondered how I could speak on inner power while a slave to those socially-acceptable substances. I couldn't. My fingers wouldn't let me tap the keyboard. My mind was unfocused, foggy, and anxious. The time to shift was upon me. I had no choice but to release those substances from my life.

Before I quit caffeine, sugar, and carbs entirely, I was scared to. I was scared to admit I felt scared. I believed I needed them to function. How would I be, who would I be without these chemicals I was so accustomed to? I didn't want or have time to be tired, although I was chronically fatigued. Ironically, I had little energy left. I had little desire to dance and walk. I couldn't imagine how I could possibly function without tea in the morning and afternoons. I ran on fumes every evening after seven pm. I had no other choice but to see who I was on the other side of these chemical dependencies. I owed it to myself to experience the person I was without it. My inner-geeky scientist had a chemical experiment to perform with unknown outcomes to step into. When to start became the question. "Someday," was my answer for so long. That is the answer for most of us—knowing that a shift is needed but not feeling ready to make the change. Then the question becomes, "When will I be ready?"

Never, that's when. Until there is no other choice but to be ready. Until we can't ignore what is the truth about our problems. When we stop blaming others and our circumstance for our issues, we will be ready to take command of our own existence.

I was ready when I had to become ready. The only alternative was to give up entirely on my health and medicate myself for every symptom that came out of the root cause; unmanaged stress and poor nutrition. Instead, I gave myself some space to feel my tiredness as I went through the few weeks of withdrawal into the depths of journeying into refining my alignment.

I'm not one to give up on anything, especially myself. As blocked as I have been, slowly growing at my own rate, I have never stopped trying to understand the why, the what, and the how. The compulsion to grow has been my saving grace. Slowing myself down helped me see why I chose to reach for harmful foods that made me feel like crap. I was well accustomed to feeling like crap, and when I owned it, I taught myself how to feel better with a lot of support and a solid nutritional plan of action to eradicate cravings for crap. Now that I'm not consuming sugar, high-carb foods, and other gut-destroying processed food, I am giving my nervous system space to do its "rest and repair" work. And what do you know, it's working quite well! With the disease feeders / insults removed, the body, mind, and emotions are doing what it is designed to do, heal and restore what was damaged.

My health improves by the day and my energy is vital like never before. Having the support I need now; I am making massive progress in a matter of months. I'm on my way to putting my Hashimoto's into remission through nutrition, movement, and stillness. My auto-immune dis-ease is not a life sentence; it is a great blessing, illuminating cause and effect and the consequences of long-term, poorly-managed stress. My plan is to stick with my program of ancestral nutrition, moderate exercise, and stress-reduction. I'm praying I haven't reached the point of no return as far as the damage done to my thyroid, but I accept it if that's the case. Over four decades of damage takes more than a just a few months to fully repair. Hopefully, my story will inspire people to manage stress in healthy ways, get the help they need to prevent irreversible damage and manage what life hands us with grace.

Fear is the disease, love is the cure

Honesty, then, is the cure for addiction and can stop the progression of many preventable dis-eases. What if our issues are, at their root, an addiction to scarcity, chaos, denial, disappointment, and hopelessness? If that's so, the solution to our problems is awakening the awareness of our innate abundance, acceptance, calm, and trust. Are we destined to learn this only after having received a diagnosis or a threat of some major ill consequence of some kind? Perhaps. Again, change only happens if it must.

Contrast illuminates truth. EmBODYment creates honesty at its most physical. Inner-alignment comes out humility, and out of that, honesty. Truth leads to emPOWERment, it is the path to health and wellness. There are no hacks or shortcuts. Honest responsibility is the high road and the only road to true wellness for us and for the rest of the world.

EmPOWERment lies in our own personal values. It's essential not to impulsively follow what others think, say, and do. Our own unique truths, beliefs, and perspectives contain our power. Fearing our power originated from being overpowered by others. That piece of code is needed to upgrade the program to our emPOWERment. Our power is in our confidence, honest, and compassionate expression. To be emPOWERed is to be a leader.

True leaders feel

Leadership lies in being your own sovereign being. Change begins with leaders standing up for their preferences based on their feelings and values. True leaders are sovereign and emotionally intelligent. They do not cower to others when it matters most. They voice their feelings, beliefs, and opinions. They provide solutions to problems. They listen, and they follow sensible guidance. A leader possesses the emotional traits of courageousness, confidence, and intuition.

In spite of your own very human trepidation, claim leadership of your own life and the lives you affect by bringing alignment to it.

Pillars of health

To reiterate, personal health consists of the mental, emotional, and physical aspects of our being. Cultural health is made from spiritual, social, and environmental factors. Personal and broader financial health relates to each aspect in today's world. People use financial concerns to say they "can't afford" eating healthy, when it is really a matter of priorities as to where they place their values and their dollars. Economic health is totally out of alignment from the standpoint of responsible resource management on most nations and global scales, given the societal concerns of today. Wealth and money overshadow personal and global health and wellness to such an extreme that they are used to bypass concerns for accountability and sustainability. With this continuance of minimizing the personal and environmental health education, the future is bleak. Institutionalized incompetence and ignorance of such realities only benefit the few self-interested corporations for short gains. From a world view perspective over centuries of time, what are these corporate giants investing in other than the short-term in sacrifice for the future?

The cultural background of people is the biggest health influencer so long as people aren't aware of its influence. The norms and diets of the groups we associate with profoundly influence personal health. Only by being aware of these social forces can one understand the nuances of cultural wellness, or else we suffer from its imbalances. The prevalence of preventable dis-eases and problems caused by refined foods, excessive alcohol, and other substance abuse are good examples of societal dysfunction when it comes to personal and social health feeding each other. People can influence the health of the culture when they decide to do something different. Following a low-carb, ketogenic or paleo diet, for example, changes the demand for food supply. These new dietary lifestyles, as well as the dairy-free and gluten-free trends, completely shift market trends. As organics grow in popularity, conventional food demand is shrinking, and supplies will respond in kind. Trends are adapting to new, healthier, and responsibly sustainable needs. It's an exciting time for personal and global wellness, but there seems to be a great divide. People are either stuck in the old unhealthy programs, participating in the dull and dismal same old song and dance among archaic societies, or reorienting themselves towards their next upgrade in health.

My offering

I've done my absolute best to demonstrate how personal health upgrades are executed and how society is capable and moving towards a sustainable, healthy future. Simple, not easy. I feel compelled to help with that.

The foundation of what I offer to individuals and groups is based on the three aspects of our being: mental, physical, and emotional. This reveals how sensible nutrition, low-impact, freeing movement, and compassionate stillness practices deliver true wellness to anyone willing to grow into their healthfulness.

I serve people ready to upgrade their scarcity program to abundance. Knowing is the first step to progressing on a health journey, and emPOWERment only comes with the humility of asking for support. On an individual basis, many people suffer from isolation but distrust, and are curious about how they can resolve their chronic struggles with pain and inner turmoil. I train people to honor it all, emBODY their truths, and find alignment through self-compassion. For groups, I invite organization, business, and corporation pioneers looking to support their human capital through better employee health programming. I utilize one-on-one ergonomic wellness training packages, interactive team-building wellness workshops, and presentations that provide actionable tools for my sensible and practical integrated health approach. I offer comprehensive, customized wellness programs based on the unique needs of each specific group.

I invite you to join us, who live in the next paradigm of collaborative support in the growth of abundant wellness. May you discover your enough-ness, your multi-dimensionality, and wins within you. Your miraculous heart, mind, body, and wins reach far beyond yourself and extend to others and the world. I celebrate your arrival.

Align your body, align your life, align the world. Imagine that. I believe it can be done. Remember Einstein's words: "Imagination is more important than knowledge."

"Challenge yourself; it's the only path that leads to growth."

- Morgan Freeman

Author's Note

Who do I think I am?

What nerve.

So full of myself.

(Who else might I be full of?)

I'd never have written this book if I didn't learn alignment to my own brutal honesty and integrity. I believe that subconsciously, that's why I was led by my desire to write it. As I dove into this project, I greatly minimized the negative effects caffeine and "carbage" foods were having on my physical, mental, and emotional health. I had massive upgrades of my own in order to share all of these truths. This creative work set me aligned my actions gracefully with my convictions, facing my demons all along the way. This was no linear process; it was messy and disorganized at first, I confronted and overcame my destructive perfectionism daily. I allowed my writing be a process, releasing the expectation that it be a finished product as I drafted it. While sharing the message of alignment, emPOWERment, and emBODYment, this book profoundly reinforced each one. I walked the talk before this and now talked my walk.

I wrote this book to share my truth with the extraordinary individuals who are curious and courageous enough to read it. Thank you for being extraordinary, curious, and courageous as you make your own way in your unique and sovereign life. If I inspired those who can relate to elements of my story and my intent, this book will have served others as I have hoped. If it was an exercise only for me, I am thankful for it all. I've gotten out so much value from walking this restorative path and exploring my ever-expanding health journey, so I passionately urge you to live for the win-win-win as well. If you crave more vitality and richness in your life, my wish is that these words give you hope in the belief that it is not only possible, but probable. Remember, trust the process of your alignment and align you will.

Your body speaks; listen.

Resources

Books

Anonymous. *Alcoholics Anonymous.* (1939, 2001). Alcoholics Anonymous World Services, Inc.

Anonymous. *Recovery Dharma: How to Use Buddhist Practices and Principles to Heal the Suffering of Addiction.* (2019) Recovery Dharma.

Anonymous *Twelve Steps and Twelve Traditions.* (1952, 1981). Alcoholics Anonymous World Services, Inc.

Dass, Ram. *Be Here Now.* (1978) Lama Foundation.

Gokhale, Esther, L.Ac. *8 Steps to a Pain-Free Back.* (2008). Pendo Press.

Griffin, Kevin. *One Breath at A Time: Buddhism and The Twelve Steps.* (2004, 2018). Rodale Books.

Miller, Olive Beaupre. *The Little Engine That Could: The Original Tale from 1920.* (1920, 2020). Racehorse for Young Readers.

KrishnaMurti, Jiddu. *Think On These Things.* (1964). Harpur & Row.

Silverstein, Shel. *The Missing Piece Meets the Big O.* (2006). HarperCollins.

Mitchell, Stephen. *Tao Te Ching: A New English Version.* (1988). HarpurCollins.

Paulus, Trina. *Hope For the Flowers.* (1972). Paulist Press.

Van Der Kolk, Bessel, M.D. *The Body Keeps the Score: Brain, Mind, and Body in The Healing of Trauma.* (2014). Penguin Books.

Walker, Pete. *The Tao of Fully Feeling: Harvesting Forgiveness Out of Blame.* (1995). Azure Coyote Publishing.

Podcasts & YouTube Channels

Carnivore Doctor. Dr. Lisa Weiderman. Thirteen-year carnivore diet advocate and optometrist for thirty years. YouTube: https://bit.ly/carnivoredoctor Ig: @carnivoredoctor

Food Junkies: Recovery from Food Addiction Podcast. Vera Tarman, M.D. Clinical physician, author, food addiction expert and recovering food addict. https://www.youtube.com/c/VeraTarmanMD Ig:@dr_vera_tarman

Food Slain Podcast. Michelle Klieger, Agricultural Economist. Digging deep into our dirty food supply chain that are compromising our health, our environment, and our economy. https://bit.ly/FoodSlainYTC Ig: @foodslain https://foodslain.com/

Hopono'pono Prayer Meditation. Jason Stephenson – Sleep Meditation Music, YouTube Channel. This simple forgiveness prayer is useful for letting go of resentments. https://youtu.be/yDJYZXlsASg

Keto Carnivore Fertility Doc. Robert Kiltz, MD. Long-time fertility specialist and Keto-Carnivore Diet educator. https://www.youtube.com/c/DrRobKiltzMD Ig: @doctorkiltz

Shawn Baker MD. Co-Founder of Revero, Orthopaedic Surgeon, Athlete, Author, and Speaker. https://www.youtube.com/channel/UC5apkKkeZQXRSDbqSalG8CQ

What You're Craving Podcast. Molly Carmel, LCSW-R Therapist. An eating disorder survivor, and author of Breaking Up with

Sugar, helping people find a sustainable relationship with food and themselves.

YouTube: https://www.youtube.com/user/mollycarmel

Ig: @mollycarmel

Recommended Sites Online

Better Help: Affordable, private therapy online. Betterhelp.com

Eat Wild: Getting Wild Nutrition from Modern Food. Directory website to locate local meat producers in your area. Jo Robinson, creator of the site and investigative journalist spent the past 15 years scouring research journals for information on how we can restore vital nutrients to our fruits, vegetables, meat, eggs, and dairy products. EatWild.com

Mikhaila Peterson: CEO, Podcaster, Lifestyle & Diet Blogger. Mikhailapeterson.com

Revero: Reverse Chronic Diseases. Restoring Health with the Carnivore Elimination Diet. Community Support and Resources for health and weight loss. Revero.com

Why We Do What We Do by Tony Robbins. Our most basic six needs explained and how we prioritize them uniquely. bit.ly/TonyRobinsWhyWeDoWhatWeDo

Recovery Support (most are free)

12 Step and other Recovery Groups can be a powerful step along the path to learn awareness around any addiction, although it is not a substitute for professional support. Remember, connection is the antidote to addiction.

<u>Drugs and Alcohol</u>

Alcoholics Anonymous (AA)

– http://www.alcoholics-anonymous.org

Co-Anon/ Cocaine Anonymous

– http://www.co-anon.org/

Narcotics Anonymous (NA)

– http://www.na.org/

<u>Food & Drink Groups</u>

Caffeine Addicts Anonymous (CAFAA)

– https://caffeineaddictsanonymous.org/

Eating Disorders Anonymous (EDA)

– http://www.eatingdisordersanonymous.org/

Food Addicts Anonymous (FA)

– http://foodaddictsanonymous.org/

Food Addicts in Recovery Anonymous (FARA)

– http://www.foodaddicts.org/

Overeaters Anonymous

– http://www.oa.org/

Sugar & Carb Addicts Anonymous

– https://scaa.club/

SUGARx Global

– https://www.sugarxglobal.com/

<u>For The Family</u>

Adult Children of Alcoholics

– http://www.adultchildren.org/

Al-Anon/Alateen

– http://www.al-anon.alateen.org/

Co-Dependents Anonymous
– http://www.codependents.org/
Families Anonymous
– http://www.familiesanonymous.org/
Parents Anonymous
– http://www.parentsanonymous.org/

Non-Specific Addiction Support
Recovery Dharma Online (RDO)
– https://recoverydharma.online/
Recovery 2.0. Life Beyond Addiction.

-https://r2o.com/

Other Addiction 12 Step Recovery Groups
Debtors Anonymous
– http://debtorsanonymous.org/
Gamblers Anonymous
– http://www.gamblersanonymous.org/
Hepatitis C Anonymous
– http://www.hcvanonymous.com/
Heroin Anonymous
– http://www.heroin-anonymous.org/
HIV AIDS Anonymous
– http://www.hivanonymous.com/
Kleptomaniacs and Shoplifters Anonymous
– http://www.shopliftersanonymous.com/
Marijuana Anonymous
– http://www.marijuana-anonymous.org/
Methadone Anonymous

– http://www.methadonesupport.org/
Nicotine Anonymous
– http://www.nicotine-anonymous.org/
Pills Anonymous
– http://groups.msn.com/PillsAnonymous/
Prescription Anonymous
– http://www.prescriptionanonymous.org/
Procrastinators Anonymous
– https://procrastinators-anonymous.org/
Recovering Couples Anonymous
– http://www.recovering-couples.org/
Schizophrenics Anonymous
– http://sanonymous.com/
Self Mutilators Anonymous
– http://www.selfmutilatorsanonymous.org/
Spenders Anonymous
– http://www.spenders.org/
Survivors of Incest Anonymous
– http://www.siawso.org/
Trauma Anonymous
– http://traumaanonymous.com/
Workaholics Anonymous
– http://www.workaholics-anonymous.org/

Sex & Love Addictions
Love Addicts Anonymous
– http://www.loveaddicts.org/
Sexaholics Anonymous
– http://www.sa.org/

Sex Addicts Anonymous

– http://www.sexaa.org/

Sex and Love Addicts Anonymous

– http://www.slaafws.org/

Sexual Compulsive Anonymous

– http://www.sca-recovery.org/

Sexual Recovery Anonymous

– http://sexualrecovery.org/

Crisis Support

SAMHSA National Helpline (Substance Abuse and Mental Health Services Administration), 24hrs/7days a week, 365-days-a-year. 1-800-662-HELP (4357)

Suicide Hotline: Dial 988, https://988lifeline.org/

Courses & Community Support

Awaken Your Inner Author, www.awakenyourinnerauthor.com

Download Melissa's Magic system to finally write the book that's trapped in your mind and heart.

As aspiring authors, we dream of our book creating a movement for the world and financial freedom for ourselves. But far too often, what happens instead is the soul-crushing experience of publishing your book only to have sales fall flat, momentum stunted, and your potentially life-changing book reaches precious few people. We are dedicated to making sure your story ends quite differently -- with you creating the impact and income that you desire from your book. That's where the publishing partnership with Ultimate Vida comes in. Grounded with decades of experience in online marketing and building sound business models around books, we help authors sidestep land-mines and reach their goals by providing actionable data (like title and cover testing), a deep and intimate understanding of who your audience actually is (which is bound to surprise you), strategic advice on offerings beyond the book, and ongoing monthly income opportunities that far exceed book royalties. Reach out to melissa@uncorpedinfluence.com to discuss strategies to make a splash with your book and incorporate the Ultimate Vida community experience and course as a new revenue stream.

Join the Ultimate Vida Freedom Circle

Your Secret Weapon To Kiss Your Job Goodbye in as Little as 77 Days, Build an Online Tribe, and Leave a Legacy

---

As an Ultimate Vida Freedom Circle Member, you can:

- Create a baseline of time and financial freedom while doing work you love
- Access proprietary data and strategies to blissfully use your newfound emPOWERment as a guide in your entrepreneurial journey
- Get FREE access to our flagship Freedom Blueprint course, which sells on its own for $1,500
- Use your newfound freedom to focus on health, wellness, relationships, and purpose...the things that make life worth living
- Connect with the world's most epic tribe of freedom seekers to enrich your life, help you achieve your goals, and form lifelong friendships
- Earn supplemental income or even life-changing monthly money by referring others into the community

---

Enjoy the Community for FREE for 14 days!

www.ultimatevida.com/align

About the Author

Wellness trainer and speaker, LisaBeth uses her health education and body awareness techniques to support inner growth and alignment to well-being. She illuminates a practical path to emBODYment. By embracing your desire to feel your best, LisaBeth facilitates un-learning of undesired habits by questioning your past conditioning to strengthen the inner guidance of your intuition.

Virtue is her guiding force. Her drive, preferences, and values gave her the gumption to share through this book about how her personal story influenced the work she provides the world. LisaBeth intends to inspire others to bravely follow their hunches and live their best and most healthful life, actualizing a unique, creative existence that resembles no one else.

She lives in New England, for her love of the region and all four seasons.

Printed in Great Britain
by Amazon

85983659R00190